TOXIC PEARL

Pacific Northwest Shellfish Companies' Addiction to Pesticides?

A True Story

The story of the Toxic Pearl belongs on the bookshelf next to *A Bitter Fog: Herbicides and Human Rights* by Carol Van Strum, and *Fresh Fruit, Broken Bodies: Migrant Farmworkers in the United States* by Seth Holmes. It's a story of invasive species, pesticides, and a community directly impacted by the shellfish industry. The author is clearly inspired by the academic conclusions and bravery of Rachel Carson. Thank you for bringing this story to light and for your work exposing aerial applications and other pesticide controls in the fragile ecosystem of Willapa Bay and Grays Harbor. The future of oyster farming in Washington State depends on the industry's ability to adopt sustainable cultural and management strategies.

—Megan Dunn
Healthy People and Communities Program Director
Northwest Center for Alternatives to Pesticides (NCAP)

TOXIC PEARL

Pacific Northwest
Shellfish Companies'
Addiction to Pesticides?

A True Story
by M. Perle

Toxic Pearl
Pacific Northwest Shellfish Companies' Addiction to Pesticides?
copyright © 2018

Paperback ISBN: 978-0-578-40162-1

Toxic Pearl: Pacific Northwest Shellfish Companies' Addiction to Pesticides?
1. Pacific Northwest Shellfish Companies; 2. Willapa Bay, WA; 3. Grays Harbor, WA; 4. Non-native Pacific oysters; 5. Burrowing shrimp; 6. Eelgrass; 7. Duckgrass; 8. Pesticides in shellfish; 9. Imazamox; 10. Imazapyr; 11. Imidacloprid; 12. Carbaryl; 13. Glyphosate; 14. Regulatory Capture; 15. Spartina; 16. Shoalwater Bay Tribe; 17. Social and environmental justice; 18. Colonialism. I. TITLE.

Unless otherwise noted, all photos were provided by: *Laura Hendricks, Coalition to Protect Puget Sound, and Case Inlet Shoreline Association*

Cover photo originally published at: *http://protectourshorelinenews.blogspot.com/2014/07/bee-killing-imidacloprid-banned-in.html*

Manufactured in the United States of America

FIRST EDITION

A STORY ABOUT...
Regulatory Capture

Questionable Science

Creative Marketing

A STORY ABOUT...
An industry that brands itself as sustainable

... and growing shellfish and fish in

Pristine Water while using Pesticides

Quote from *Willapa Bay Oysters* documentary, "If you've ever eaten an oyster from Willapa Bay, welcome to the world it came from."

Carbaryl-spraying helicopter killing native species to make way for non-native oysters.
(Source: Department of Ecology)

Contents

Dedicated to
my Mom

Abbreviation Key

Ad Hoc Coalition for Willapa Bay & Washington Toxics Coalition	Willapa Coalitions
All Known, Available, and Reasonable Methods of Treatment	AKART
American Bird Conservancy	ABC
Aquaculture Stewardship Council	ASC
Burrowing Ghost & Mud Shrimp	Burrowing Shrimp
Burrowing Shrimp Committee	Committee
Clean Water Act	CWA
Department of Agriculture	Agriculture
Department of Ecology	Ecology (WDOE, DOE)
Department of Fish & Wildlife	DFW, WDFW
Department of Fisheries	Fisheries, DOF
Department of Natural Resources	DNR
Environmental Impact Statement	EIS
Environmental Protection Agency	EPA
Executive Ethics Management Board	Ethics Board
Food and Drug Administration	FDA
Imidacloprid	Neonic
Integrated Pest Management Plan	IPMP
National Marine Fisheries Service	NMFS
National Pollutant Discharge Elimination System	NPDES
Noxious Weed Control Board	Weed Board
Pollution Control Hearings Board	Board
Public Employees for Environmental Responsibility	PEER

Shoalwater Bay Tribe	Shoalwater
The Monsanto Company	Monsanto
University of Washington	UW
US Centers for Disease Control	CDC
US Department of Agriculture	USDA
Willapa/Grays Harbor Oyster Growers Association	Shellfish Association
Washington State University	WSU
Zostera japonica	Duckgrass
Zostera marina	*Marina*

INTRODUCTION

In 2013, the shellfish industry of Willapa Bay, located on the coast of Washington State near the mouth of the Columbia River, partnered with the state's two large land grant universities to produce a documentary about the 160-year old Willapa Bay oyster industry. This seven-part nostalgic documentary is narrated by Washington State University's communications professor emeritus, Glenn Johnson, recognizable as the "Voice of the Cougs"—the public address announcer for its football and men's basketball teams.

In a warm and refined professional radio voice, Glenn Johnson introduces the *Willapa Bay Oysters* documentary with, "This is the story of families, individuals, and companies building their futures on the foundations of their ancestors. This is THEIR industry, through THEIR eyes."

Toxic Pearl tells another side of the story, not told by the shellfish industry, state agencies, or state universities funded by the public.

PREFACE

This story is intended to be an antidote to the *Willapa Bay Oysters* documentary, and to a state and industry that extol the virtues of the shellfish industry, but which doesn't talk about a half-century of pesticide use, with no end in sight. The general and consuming public doesn't know about the pesticide use in Washington State marine waters. *Toxic Pearl* tells this story.

Widespread pesticide use began in 1963, and has been in continuous use ever since. The first pesticide Washington State (the state) allowed was carbaryl, which was used to kill two species of native shrimp that some say loosen the substrate and causes mono-crop-grown, non-native, invasive Pacific oysters to sink and suffocate.

Since 1963, carbaryl has been sprayed by helicopter and by hand into Willapa Bay and Grays Harbor—fifty years where the chemical has contaminated the water column, the sediments, and has killed more than 10,000,000 animals (as estimated by the state) with each spray event.

Carbaryl is reportedly used in Hood Canal and Puget Sound, but without state permits. One of these native burrowing shrimp species appears to be on a path to extinction, yet the state is still considering ways to kill them.

As the result of an appeal initiated by two small oyster growers against Ecology and the Willapa/Grays Harbor Oyster Growers Association (Shellfish Association), they were supposed to phase out pesticide use by 2012. Instead, these companies and the state invested almost two decades and untold resources into eliminating regulatory hurdles to switch to imidacloprid, a potent neurotoxin never intended for aquatic use. These companies sprayed carbaryl in 2013 in violation of the settlement agreement, and then sprayed imidacloprid in the bays in 2014 as "research and development." Imidacloprid, widely known for contributing to the decline of bees and other pollinators, can also devastate aquatic invertebrates and the animals that rely on them for food. The state approved the use of imidacloprid in 2015, and that story is told in this book.

Currently, shellfish companies in Willapa Bay use pesticides to kill eelgrasses. Although all eelgrass was once protected as critical habitat by the state, shellfish companies were successful in getting one non-native eelgrass de-listed. This allowed them to begin eradicating that one, yet the pesticide also kills the beloved native eelgrass. Both provide critical habitat for a wealth of species and are relied upon by migratory ducks and geese along the coastal Pacific Flyway, one of the largest migration routes in the world. Defoliation of these eelgrasses in Willapa Bay continues to this day, while the state has suspended meaningful annual bird counts.

Washington State leads the nation in the production of mono-crop-farmed non-native oysters and clams, and the industry located on Willapa Bay is described as "vast" and "booming," producing millions of pounds of shellfish per year, worth upwards of $40 million. Oysters and clams are grown for food, yet are also considered indicators of ecosystem health because they act as "bio-sinks," concentrating and retaining bio-toxins such as pesticides, PCBs, chemical wastes, and by-products (heavy metals and coliform bacteria) from agricultural runoff.

Toxic Pearl is an important story because of the adverse impacts on the ecosystem from the widespread use of these pesticides, coupled with the ability of the farmed oysters and clams to retain toxins. Those are two good reasons to discontinue this practice.

On top of bay-wide pesticide use, this industry and state treat Willapa Bay like a large farm—converting upwards of 17,000 acres of native tidelands into mono-cropped non-native shellfish beds—with their eyes on another 13,000 acres of estuarine habitat. The state sold these tidelands, and even though they are part of a sensitive estuarine ecosystem, the state now says they don't have authority to regulate—or even monitor—what these shellfish companies do on those lands to prevent impacts to the ecosystem.

Toxic Pearl gives voice to six citizen activists who fought for decades to end the use of pesticides in Washington's marine waters: Larry Warnberg, Ernie Summers, Herb Whitish, Fritzi Cohen, Marcial Hunter (who asked that his real name not be used to protect his privacy), and Laura Hendricks. *Toxic Pearl* is their story. All were interviewed for this book—except Ernie Summers and Herb Whitish—both who have passed but left written legacies. The state and industry viewpoint is told with a focus on action because—as the adage goes—actions speak louder than words.

This book also gives voice to the millions of animals who died excruciating deaths from carbaryl, a potent toxic chemical with the same mode of action as chemicals used in warfare, and to those that may have died from under-studied secondary effects.

The author is concerned about loss of biological diversity, species extinction, as well as use of toxic pesticides, and wrote this book to bring awareness to this pesticide use—especially the current use of imazamox in Willapa Bay. Hopefully those working in the shellfish industry—hard-working people who care about the environment—will join the movement to end the use of pesticides.

~

Here are a few navigational aids to the structure of this book:

This story is not a precise linear progression of time, but it does move from historical to current day.

The first few chapters are set in the years 2012 to 2014. Subsequent chapters are either an historical summary that spans decades, or a chapter about one of the six featured citizen activists, placed within the time progression, more or less. An appendix at the end of the book lists shellfish companies and individuals expressly permitted by the state to spray pesticides into marine waters. These names have not been changed.

The broadest term "pesticide" is used in this narrative for both insecticides and herbicides. A pesticide is a substance intended to prevent, destroy, repel, or mitigate a pest and they are grouped according to the type of pests they control. For example, fungicides kill fungi, insecticides kill insects, and herbicides kill plants.

In some instances, people's names have been changed to protect their privacy, or out of fear of retaliation. In those instances, the first use of the name is accompanied by an asterisk (*).

Finally, since some companies are involved with both oysters and clams, and some just oysters or just clams, the broadest term "shellfish company" or shellfish companies, is used instead of toggling back and forth between oyster company and clam company. And since not all shellfish companies use pesticides, the term "companies" is used and the term "industry" is used sparingly.

Chapter 1: All That Glitters

In 2012, Jen Harper* was hired by the Washington Department of Natural Resources (DNR) to manage tideland leases. The majority of those leases were for shellfish in Willapa Bay and Grays Harbor, coastal bays that Harper was familiar with having worked as a charter-fishing deckhand out of Westport when she was young.

Before landing this job, Harper had worked for ports on Puget Sound until, she says, she burned out after twenty years with few vacations, so she quit. After a few years off, Harper saw an aquatic lease management job advertised by DNR, and applied. She was elated when she got the job.

Harper had enough management under her belt, with plenty of gray hair to show for it, and she just wanted a less stressful job with work she could enjoy. The job also appealed to her because it required time spent on boats and on the tidelands, and an intriguing first assignment: a market study of shellfish rents in her coastal territory.

Shortly after her orientation, Harper began reading through the leases and found something she thought was peculiar. Each lease had the same attachment, an exhibit allowing the tenants to use *pesticides* on state-owned tidelands.

Pesticides? she wondered. Specifically, a pesticide called carbaryl. Something seemed wrong. So Harper consulted with her superiors and sure enough, the information was correct—the tenants were using carbaryl. In a way, she didn't want to know more … spraying any toxin into fragile marine ecosystems was beyond her comprehension. A few months later, she joined Ecology staff to observe helicopter spraying of carbaryl on the tidelands of Willapa Bay—it was their job to monitor wind speeds during the spraying. Harper asked if she could tag along. While there, she observed workers out on the tideflats, and commented to Ecology staff that it looked like they might have been sprayed. She was told that the direct spraying of people was not uncommon, but that their scope was to just monitor wind speeds.

"Raw oysters on the half shell are a big hit among a lot of consumers, especially a lot of the younger generation, and we try to capitalize on that. I'm not so sure that they understand all the work that goes into that product sitting on the half shell. There's a lot that goes into that one slurp you take."
—Quote from *Willapa Bay Oysters* documentary.

Annual carbaryl spraying killed more than 10,000,000 animals each year, as estimated by the state in its 1992 environmental analysis. Harvest of shellfish (off-plot), fish, and crab was not suspended during the spraying, or afterwards. (Source: Ecology)

CHAPTER 1: ALL THAT GLITTERS

Harper's work on the shellfish market study progressed, and she found ample market-priced leases between shellfish companies and *private* tideland owners to conclude that the state was not charging a fair market rent. The leases she managed charged only a land rent, and no production rent or share of the harvest. Such a production rent was charged by DNR shellfish leases on Hood Canal and Puget Sound, but not on Willapa Bay or Grays Harbor. In addition, while DNR was not charging a production rent in these two major shellfish producing bays, private tideland owners WERE charging a market rent.

Why wasn't the state charging a market rent? Harper found what she thought was the explanation: prior DNR staff attempts to charge a market rent were thwarted by political pressure and by the Pacific Coast Shellfish Growers Association, based in Olympia, which advised its members not to pay their rent. So the flat rent continued for decades with no change.

Harper estimated that the state was foregoing millions annually by not charging a market rent, and what rent DNR did collect didn't even cover costs to manage the leasing program.

She concluded the study in 2014. Harper's supervisor crafted several options for how to negotiate market rents, and submitted this to the DNR Aquatic Division management. Harper said she enjoyed this interesting assignment, and looked forward to bringing these lease rents in line with what the state was charging on the inland waters.

When the decision came down to not pursue a market rent, Harper was dumbfounded. She was told that DNR management didn't want to upset the shellfish industry, which might retaliate in a variety of ways through the state legislature, particularly with an aquatic habitat conservation plan, which had not yet been adopted by the agency. Harper says she kept finding creative ways to transition to the market rent, but she was warned off, so she dropped mention of the study or its results, and commiserated in spirit with her long retired DNR colleagues from the 1980s who had hit a similar wall: political power.

Things weren't going as she had envisioned: annual helicopter spraying of pesticides to kill two species of native burrowing shrimp to benefit non-native shellfish culture was ongoing, and the agency's refusal to charge fair market rent made her question if this was the right job for her after all.

Then Harper was instructed to terminate the lease of a small-time harvester of burrowing shrimp in those bays being sprayed annually by shellfish companies to kill the same shrimp. The reason? Concerns about the shrimp population. Which made no sense.

Lone Shrimper

Michael Lewis* was a long time DNR tenant who rented tidelands that Harper managed. His lease was located on Ellen Sands, a large inter-tidal landform in Willapa Bay where he harvested burrowing shrimp for bait. Ellen Sands is accessible only by boat, and only on a low tide. Willapa Bay is an unusually shallow coastal bay in Washington State, just north of the mouth of the Columbia River and an estuary where freshwater running off the land mingles with the salty ocean, creating one of the most productive ecosystems in the world. Animals have come here to eat, reproduce, and rest from long migratory journeys for millennia.

In recent geologic history, Willapa Bay had been part of the mouth of the Columbia, but the mighty river migrated southward. Before it was dammed, the Columbia dropped sandy sediments along its former course that currents then sculpted into Long Beach Peninsula, a 28-mile barrier spit that forms the western shore of Willapa Bay. The Columbia also left sandy sediments deposited throughout the interior of the bay. Fully half of the bay is exposed at lowest tide. Novice mariners, especially ones skippering boats they don't own, are strongly advised to stay out of Willapa Bay altogether, or to hang with a local long enough to gain some knowledge. Where are the navigable channels? Do they move? At what tide can you cut corners?

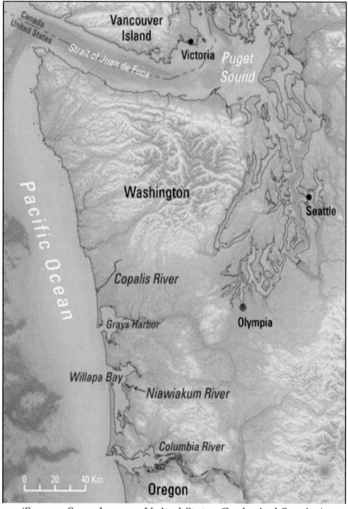

(Source: Soundwaves, United States Geological Service)

Early European navigators found it too shallow and treacherous for their ships to enter, and named it Shoalwater Bay. A hundred years later, the name was changed to Willapa Bay by aspiring industrialists hungry for large ships and vessels to come up the Willapa River. The treacherous sounding "Shoalwater Bay" just didn't cut it. The tidal range in Willapa Bay is from an extreme low of -2 feet to an extreme high of +12 feet. When the tide drops to the +5-foot level, it is time to head for shore or risk getting stuck on the tideflats. But stuck on the tideflats is exactly where Michael Lewis scratched out a living, and Jen Harper became familiar with his operation.

Once he would secure his unnamed boat with an anchor, Lewis looked for telltale holes—shrimp burrows—before he unloaded his gear, which comprised buckets and two hundred feet of hose and a high-pressure nozzle. His typical method of operation was to transfer his buckets and hose onto the sand. Since the pump intake had to be submerged in water, the pump stayed with the boat while he hunted across the tideflats, pulling the hose. The limiting factor for the area he could shrimp without moving his boat wasn't the two hundred feet of hose, it was the weight of the hose filled with water.

There are two native Willapa Bay burrowing shrimp: mud shrimp and ghost shrimp. Lewis harvested ghost shrimp, so named because of their transparency and pale color. For brevity in this book, these two species of burrowing shrimp are simply referred to as shrimp, unless otherwise noted. These shrimp have no central spine or bone skeleton, so they're classified as invertebrates. Instead, they have a hard external shell—an exoskeleton—to protect their fragile bodies.

Native shrimp create intricate, complex burrows of tunnels and rooms in the sand, with passages that come close to other passages, but just far enough away that the burrow is structurally sound. The burrows are about three feet deep. Shrimp are brilliant architects of soil, so much so that other marine creatures use the burrows as well.

One of the many native species targeted by the non-native shellfish companies.

Mud Shrimp (*Upogebia pugettensis*).
(Source: John Chapman, Oregon State University)

The shrimp fill an important ecological niche in the marine environment as a critically important food source for a wide range of native and migratory species including: crab, smelt, herring, salmon, flounder, sculpin, cutthroat trout, white sturgeon, and especially green sturgeon. Some fish eat juvenile shrimp and larvae while they float in water; others, like the bottom feeding green and white sturgeon, eat adult and juvenile shrimp by filtering sediments.

Even gray whales rely on the shrimp when these large marine mammals pull into Willapa Bay to dine while on their northward and southward migrations. Big, crater-like depressions are similar to the dirty dishes left behind by whales as they scoop up the sediments, sieve out the water, and swallow the shrimp. Fish, crab, and whales all prey on the various life-stages of the shrimp when the tide is high; shorebirds and shrimpers, like Lewis, prey on juvenile and adult shrimp when the tide is low.

"Every time I go out there I think about all those who came before me—Indians, explorers, other fishermen," Lewis said in an interview with *National Fisherman*. But when Harper entered the picture, Lewis' shrimping days were almost over, and Harper played her role.

The tideflats are visible when the tide is out, but the shrimp are not. The shrimp live beneath the surface of the sediments in intertidal areas: invisible, unknown, not fully understood, and flat out not appreciated by most people. Shrimp prefer the middle to low intertidal zones. Ghost shrimp habitat is distinguished by numerous holes that signal the entrances and exits of their burrows, which are the signs that Lewis looked for. Sometimes though, what Lewis thought was a shrimp burrow entrance or exit turned out to be the entrance for some other sediment dweller.

Shrimp burrow for protection from predators like Lewis, and for reproduction and food. Their burrows protect the shrimp's soft bodies, while their burrowing provides food as they pump water through the tunnels and glean microscopic plants and other animals from the sediment particles and water. Not only do shrimp burrows provide habitat for other species in highly evolved symbiotic relationships, some of their roommates cannot survive without them.

Invisible to the human eye, shrimp burrowing alters the soft sediment environment, drawing oxygen to the deeper sediment layers and increasing several-fold the surface area of the water and sediment interface. The shrimp transport algae and aquatic plants down from the sediment surface to the deeper layers. Their digging alters grain-size distribution, composition of other aquatic animals in the sediments, and the structure of microbial communities. An upland comparison is the earthworm and the invisible role they play in releasing soil nutrients for fungi and bacteria. Native shrimp are a keystone species that plays a crucial role in the way the ecosystem functions and they have done so since the Pleistocene Era, for well over 100,000 years in Willapa Bay.

The loss of these species is unthinkable and their extinction did not seem possible until recent times. The loss of these shrimp would ripple through the ecosystem, and humans won't be able to replace the functions that shrimp provide or undo the harm, were it to happen.

Lewis started harvesting shrimp when he was a young man three decades ago, before shrimp were a state-regulated fishery. Shrimp are excellent bait for steelhead and sturgeon fishing, and those are the markets for his shrimp. And since shrimp make up about half the green sturgeon diet, they are fantastic bait for sturgeon fishing. But they need to be alive.

Green and white sturgeon populations are now so low that there is no recreational or commercial harvest allowed by the state. In 2006, the National Marine Fisheries Service (NMFS) listed the green sturgeon as "threatened" under the Endangered Species Act, and there hasn't been a commercial or recreational harvest of green sturgeon since that listing. Sport fishing is allowed, with bait and barbless hooks, but if caught, they must be released. NMFS designated Willapa Bay and Grays Harbor as green sturgeon critical habitat because sturgeon are present in both bays, especially in the summer.

To flush out shrimp, Lewis would drop the intake hose into the water, pull-start his pump, insert the plastic tip of a hydraulic wand into a hole, pull the trigger, and flush a burrow. The water liquefied the sand and flushed out shrimp as well as small Dungeness crab. (Some complain that this process has an unacceptable impact on the tidelands—a shrimper can sink up to the knee in the liquefied sand.) It was common to flush other burrow inhabitants that shared space with the shrimp; they were in the burrows for protection from predators and for food, particularly young crabs. He also flushed out other subterranean animals since the water jet impacted an area much larger than the burrows.

Outside of their burrows, shrimp are fragile and lay rather helpless on the sediment surface. They can swim for short distances and move quickly backwards by flapping their skirt-like tails, but they are clearly vulnerable.

Lewis devised a tool like a French fry basket to pick up the shrimp as they struggled to get back into the sand, and would drop them into the bucket. He was expert at picking up as little sand as possible with the shrimp, which saved time later when washing the shrimp before he delivered them. Harvest days were long. He typically delivered the shrimp right after harvest to ensure they were alive, driving up to two hundred miles before his day was done.

Five to ten years ago, Lewis was harvesting six buckets per tide, but the last few years after six hours of work, he would have collected only two buckets. And, as the shrimp declined, so did the number of shrimpers. Shrimp harvest licensing began in 1991 and over the years there were as many as seven licensed shrimpers. Their numbers declined to just two in 2012, and then it was just Lewis.

Decline is a key word to describe dwindling native species in Willapa Bay. Fading icons of the Pacific Northwest include salmon, steelhead, waterfowl, and sturgeon. On the other hand, non-native species are farmed and nurtured as large monoculture crops using extraordinary methods. They are the aquatic version of eastern Washington wheat, farmed as single-species crops in Willapa Bay and Grays Harbor. The non-native crops include Pacific oyster and manila clam, and those are *not* in decline. On the contrary, conversion of native habitat to non-native shellfish habitat has increased, including the dumping (euphemistically called "frosting" by the industry, state, and federal agencies) of large barge-loads of gravel into the nearshore areas to make better habitat for the cultivation of non-native manila clams.

Come summer, like a scene straight out of *Apocalypse Now*, Lewis would hear the wop-wop-wop of the helicopter before he saw it. The sound of the pesticide-laden helicopter was his direct notice of the annual aerial assault on the shrimp with the pesticide carbaryl. Carbaryl has the same mode of action as nerve agents used in chemical warfare, and this application has been an on-going ritual for more than fifty years.

"If it's alive, it's fresh." Quote from *Willapa Bay Oysters* documentary, referring to oysters harvested from Willapa Bay.

A few of the more than 4,000,000 native burrowing shrimp estimated by the state killed under its permit and captured in this Ecology photo

For Lewis, exposure to carbaryl meant rashes on his arms, especially where the cuffs of his wet sleeves made contact with his skin. He told Harper that on spray days, and for days thereafter, he would reek of the chemical used in the shrimp kill. It also meant that his shrimp wouldn't live to qualify as live bait. They would be dead shrimp; dead bait. The annual spraying meant that the carbaryl residue he could still smell from the prior year's spraying was refreshed on a regular basis.

The targeted spray sites show as black and white boundaries on paper, but what does water know of boundaries? What do toxic chemicals know of boundaries when suspended in tidal water? The incoming tides carried the carbaryl off the sprayed tideflats and set the toxin loose in the water, carried in the bay as the water circulated, contrary to the oyster grower's claim that the carbaryl "stays on or very close to the point of application."

In this region on most days, there are two incoming and two outgoing tides. The force of the Pacific Ocean tides sweep up the pesticide and spread it in the bay, a toxic baptism for baby animals, juveniles, and adults. Millions of animals died, gasping and spasming on the sand. What happened next was a given. Birds swooped down to feed on those dying animals, en masse. Thousands of birds. One has to wonder what happened to the birds as they flew off to the next sprayed area to forage, or off to their nests to feed their young. How could birds eat that much carbaryl in all those dead and dying shrimp, fish, crab, softshell, horse clams, and cockles, and not have it affect them somehow in the short- or long-term? Did they develop mutations that they then passed on to their young?

But Lewis minded his own business and focused on shrimping. After all, he hadn't been *directly* sprayed. Not like Iner Sunderland*, a shrimper who cancelled his lease with DNR and was interviewed for this book.

Chapter 1: All That Glitters

One day, Sunderland was stranded in his boat on Russell Channel and was waiting for the incoming tide, eventually headed back to port. He sat vulnerable and helpless like a shrimp in its burrow as he and his partner were strafed—clearly visible to the anonymous pilot. After that incident of being directly sprayed with carbaryl in the early 1990s, he began having violent epileptic seizures, which continue to this day.

Sunderland's buddy, Jack Olson*, said in an interview for this book that he had been sprayed too. Olson was busy shrimping, with his pump running and didn't hear the helicopter. He was engulfed in a cloud of what he initially thought was a fog bank rolling in, then his skin started to tingle and then to violently burn. The carbaryl spray got into his eyes and they felt on fire. He couldn't see. Olson gasped as he breathed in the spray, then started to choke on his saliva as it filled his lungs. He fought his way to a small stream and covered himself with water, desperately trying to wash the carbaryl off before he passed out. If he lost consciousness, he knew he wouldn't make it. Everything was a blur. He managed to strip off some of his clothes to get the water closer to his skin. Barely able to breathe, with his body in spasm, he struggled in the pool of water to save his life. The anonymous pilot never stopped; no one came to check on him. He lived, but not without consequences. Olson developed rashes that lasted for months in the areas where his clothing had rubbed his skin.

Then there's Jim Skogen*, who, along with other people working for a shellfish company, was transported out to the tideflats and given a yellow and red placard. Skogen said in an interview that he didn't fully comprehend his role, but soon discovered that he was a *human marker* for the boundaries of this family-owned company operation. There was no escape from the spit where they placed him—he was trapped as the helicopter sprayed him repeatedly. His skin and eyes burned and boiled. It killed everything around him immediately—crabs, worms, fish, and even clams. The shrimp came to the surface in spasm. When Skogen got home that night, he fell in the kitchen as he had his first violent seizure. His mom called 911. Since that day, epileptic seizures have governed his life. A sore repeatedly flares on his hand where he held the sign. The sore has never healed, even after all these decades. He fears he may develop cancer. Life isn't the same, and he's frustrated. It's hard to drive or find work, not knowing when the next seizure will overtake him.

Dulce et Decorum Est *(excerpt)*

Gas! Gas! Quick, boys!—An ecstasy of fumbling,
Fitting the clumsy helmets just in time;
But someone still was yelling out and stumbling
And flound'ring like a man in fire or lime…
Dim, through the misty panes and thick green light,
As under a green sea, I saw him drowning.

In all my dreams, my helpless sight,
He plunges at me, guttering, choking, drowning.

Wilfred Owen, 1893-1918
a young British man killed in battle,
writing about surprise attacks of poison gas

Chapter 2: Dream Job

When shrimper Michael Lewis made his way back to the Bay Center marina one summer day in 2014, the tide was higher, which meant he could take a direct route, shaving valuable time for his remaining tasks. As he unloaded the boat, he was approached by a man he recognized, but couldn't place.

Ari Takala* introduced himself, and then Lewis remembered. A friendly man with a bit of a stutter, Takala worked for DNR, his landlord. The two men exchanged the requisite "How are you?" and then Takala explained that Jen Harper had been trying to get a hold of him, and since Takala lived nearby, he volunteered to drive down to catch him at Bay Center.

Lewis had applied for a renewal of his expired lease and it was almost ready for approval, but Takala told him that DNR wasn't going to renew his lease and that's why they had been trying to reach him.

Takala explained that DNR was terminating all its shrimp leases in Puget Sound due to concerns raised by the City of Langley on Whidbey Island. Langley representatives had successfully convinced DNR to terminate the five leases up there as a way to protect the shrimp for the gray whales.

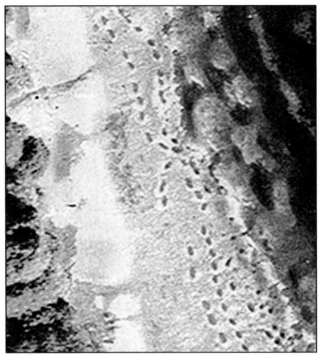

Gray whale shrimp feeding pits off Whidbey Island.
(Source: Google Maps)

Langley relied on whale watching as a tourist attraction. Whenever townspeople spotted a gray whale, they rang the town bell. In recent years, there had been fewer documented sightings of gray whales and the city was concerned that there weren't enough shrimp for the whales due to all the harvesting on public, tribal, and privately owned tidelands.

Lewis said he didn't get it. Willapa Bay is on the coast of Washington, and Puget Sound is a large inland body of water located far away.

Takala responded that he understood, but the state wanted to be consistent in its management of shrimp leases, so it was stopping all shrimping on public lands until it had time to study shrimp populations.

Soon afterwards, Harper, on behalf of DNR, sent a certified letter to Michael Lewis—the same letter sent to the shrimpers in Puget Sound—terminating his lease to shrimp on Willapa Bay. Both knew that this was his primary source of income and at 55 years, not young or in the best of shape. He had back injuries from a lifetime of fishing and logging, and his job prospects seemed bleak. Lewis lived in economically depressed Pacific County, where good paying jobs were hard to come by, even for younger workers. He called his two main shrimp buyers and broke the news to them. One called Harper in protest, but Harper told him there was nothing she could do.

Also about 55 years old with a bad back, Harper sympathized with Lewis. She says that re-entering the workforce after her sabbatical wasn't easy, and she wondered if she had been passed over for several other jobs because of her age.

This signaled the end of Harper's dream job. She'd witnessed aerial spraying of the pesticide carbaryl into an estuary she'd known since she was young; she was unable to persuade the state to charge a market rent; and now she played a role in cancelling Lewis's lease over purported concerns about shrimp populations. She says she couldn't get the image of Lewis with his measly one or two buckets per trip, compared to the state-sanctioned annual spraying that killed upwards of 4,000,000 shrimp per year, out of her mind.

CHAPTER 3: WHY?

Willapa Bay once teemed with oysters that were individually small, but they grew in giant oyster reefs. Their habitat was at and below the low-tide level because they needed consistent, cool temperatures. They lined the channels of the 43,000-acre bay. Two acres could host a million oysters.

"There were more oysters than you could imagine looking both north and south," wrote an early settler. One of the world's smallest oysters, they fit easily into the palm of a human hand. Ancient coastal settlements of Native Americans reveal huge mounds, called middens, of the small native oyster shells that date back thousands of years.

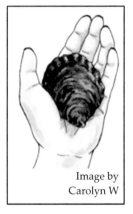

Image by Carolyn W

Virtually overnight, immigrants decimated these wild native oysters. Starting around 1848, European settlers harvested this oyster, which they named the "Olympia," and did so with a vengeance. They quickly muscled out the local Native Americans and established a lucrative industry. They scoured the bay and removed this native oyster to fuel the largest global migration in American history—the California Gold Rush. The "Road to Insanity" bordered on mass hysteria. Every day, a fortune could be made. By 1879, the trade to San Francisco had slowed, but the harvest continued, reaching a high of 90,000 bushels in 1896, then declining steadily as they removed the rest of the wild oysters from Willapa Bay. The ancient living reefs were so large that they were in the way of the boats, so the reefs were removed, used for ballast, and killed.

The female Olympia oyster fertilizes her eggs internally by filtering sperm that has been released by the males into the water column. The sperm enters the brood chamber where it fertilizes 250,000 to 300,000 eggs. The fertilized eggs then move into the mantle cavity where they develop into larvae, and stay in the female's mantle cavity for ten to twelve days while they develop their shells. By the time the larvae leave the mother oyster, they have begun to develop an eyespot and a foot.

As the larvae settle out of the water column to the substrate, they crawl, using their larval foot, looking for something suitable to attach to. Sand is not suitable and Willapa Bay is mostly sand. When the foreign settlers sold off the oysters, they removed the hard surfaces that the larvae needed for their survival. And because the harvesters did not return the empty shells (made of molecules that hundreds of generations of oysters had made into reefs and gradually recycled back into carbonate exoskeletons for the next generation of oysters) back into the water, the larvae increasingly had less and less to latch onto.

When the harvesters looked at those palm-sized oysters in their small shells, they failed to understand that the shell was the oyster's nursery, so in their haste to remove the oysters and ship them to San Francisco, they killed off the future generations. Within a scant fifty years, the European immigrants harvested the wild and native Olympia oyster to the brink of extinction in Willapa Bay. There're still there, but not in any commercial quantity, a situation referred to as a functional extinction. This once common oyster—the only one native to the West Coast of North America—is in good company. Worldwide. All wild oysters are functionally extinct.

Capture to Culture

As a result, oyster harvesters transitioned to become oyster growers, a universal transition evident in other forms of human domestication of animals from capture to culture. Starting in the late 1800s, shellfish companies began searching for an oyster that could be grown like an upland field crop, instead of wild harvest. They sought to replace the wild native oysters they had wiped out by introducing an oyster they could cultivate as a monoculture crop. From their perspective, they would simply replace the native oyster with one they could farm.

In the blink of an eye, they eliminated the role that the Olympia oyster played in the ecosystem, a role refined over thousands of years with the build-up of the huge oyster reefs—habitat built and perfected over hundreds of generations by and for the oysters. In doing so, they altered the balance between species in the bays.

The shellfish companies further disrupted that balance with the introduction of non-native Eastern oysters. "They came over by train, and they brought them in barrels. And then they planted them out on the beds," explained oyster grower Leonard Bennett in *Willapa Bay Oysters.*

Along with ice, plants and grasses were packed around the animals as a form of primitive refrigeration to keep the oysters and larvae cool and moist on the lengthy train ride to their new home. So, along with the imported Eastern oysters, shellfish companies put the exotic plants and stowaway animals into Willapa Bay. The first commercially important planting on Willapa Bay was in 1899.

Eastern oyster larvae, referred to as "spat" and once attached to a shell, were imported over many years and a small industry was maintained along the bay until about 1919, when the oysters died, likely due to the arrival of Gonyaulax, a microorganism that is toxic to oysters.

The population of Eastern oysters collapsed. Eastern oysters did not become invasive or propagate outside of the in-water farms, but the shellfish companies did introduce several non-native invasive species, including a smooth cordgrass named "spartina," which slowly took hold in Willapa Bay and other marine waters.

After giving up on the Eastern oyster, the shellfish companies went shopping in Japan. The Pacific oyster is native to Japan and has been cultivated there for centuries. Oyster spat was purchased, shipped from Japan, and the first large-scale commercial introduction in Willapa Bay occurred in 1928.

"Each year, a shipload of seed would come from Japan, and this continued for a number of years, until the war interrupted it. After the war, they took it up again," Dorwin Fosse said in *Willapa Bay Oysters*. Oysters of all ages were bundled in sea grasses and sent on two-week voyages across the Pacific Ocean, along with other plants, animals, and diseases that rapidly began to reshape the ecosystem in Willapa Bay.

The New Washington Oyster Company of Willapa Bay hired Japanese-American workers during the oyster-harvesting season. One of those workers was a young man named Giro Nagawaki. The now-elderly Nagawaki was featured in *Willapa Bay Oysters*, "All the Japanese oyster seeds used to come in a wooden box on decks of liberty ships and freighters and once it came into port, all the oyster growers... it used to be a real rat race to get your share of it. Tried to get them out as quick as you can, you know, on the beds." The companies made the same mistake with the Pacific oyster as they had with the Eastern oyster, by importing a variety of exotic plants (this time common to Japan instead of to the East Coast) packed around the oysters to keep them cool and moist.

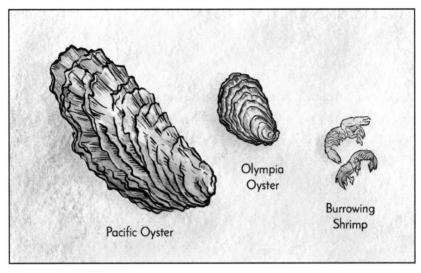

Relative size: Pacific oyster, Olympia oyster, Burrowing Shrimp

Not everyone was gung-ho about importing exotic non-native oysters. A minority of shellfish companies objected to the introduction of the non-native Pacific oyster because the Olympia oyster was making a comeback and they were concerned that it would out-compete the native Olympia oyster for food. (As suspected by the early oyster growers, the Pacific oyster does out-compete the native Olympia oyster for food.) But their concerns were pushed aside.

The companies found that the Pacific oyster could be harvested a year sooner than the smaller, slower-growing Olympia oyster, and it grew MUCH bigger. "You threw them in the water and you almost had to stand back, they grew so fast," an early oyster farmer reminisced in the book, *Willapa Bay & The Oysters*. They grew up to a foot in size. The scientific name of the Pacific oyster is *Crassostrea gigas*, translated from Latin as "giant thick oyster," which is quite appropriate. Also called "Giant Oyster," the *Crassostrea gigas* is one of the largest commercially grown oysters in the world.

"There's oysters that maybe you could get only four into a pint jar, that large. We've had oysters you couldn't even put in a pint jar," Japanese-American Richard Murakami recalled in a Washington State oral history interview from the early 1980s about the new Pacific oyster. Because of its rapid growth, fertility, and tolerance to a wide range of water temperatures and salinity, the Pacific oyster settled in Willapa Bay. By 1930, they flooded the market.

BIG BUSINESS

The industry took a turn after World War II ended. According to industry chronicler E.N. Steele, after World War II, the oyster industry entered the era of Big Business, and the spread of the giant Pacific oyster really took off. "They were getting acclimated to our areas, and they turned around and started having natural sets," said an oyster grower in *Willapa Bay Oysters*.

Another grower explains what a Pacific oyster natural set is in *Willapa Bay Oysters*:

> Natural sets, once a year if you are lucky, mean that every oyster out there will release sperm and eggs, and that will combine in the water and hopefully make baby oysters. If everything goes right, there will be billions and billions of baby oysters out there looking for things to attach to. And if you put out shell bags and loose shells, or just about anything, you'll get baby oysters.

But what he doesn't explain is that not every oyster out there spawns. Spawning is a lot of work for oysters and it interferes with their growth in several important ways. So, companies began cultivating a chromosomally modified triploid oyster designed to be sterile so it could be harvested year round, especially during summer months when fertile oysters have spawned and their tissue is too mushy to eat.[1]

And unlike the Olympia oyster, where fertilization and then brooding occur within the mother (with the first ten to twelve days of life spent inside the mother before being released into the waters), the Pacific oyster releases both eggs and sperm into the water column where fertilization occurs without the protection of the mother. This difference has noteworthy implications on the long-term survival of this species, especially as atmospheric carbon dioxide levels rise and conditions in the ocean change.

OYSTERS COLLIDE WITH NATIVE SHRIMP

Starting in the 1950s, the shellfish companies began to claim that shrimp soften the ground with their burrowing, causing the non-native oysters to suffocate, and that there was an overpopulation of shrimp—even though archeological evidence indicates the shrimp have been present there for at least 100,000 years.

Is it possible that the shellfish companies created the "conflict" between the native shrimp and their non-native oysters by placing their grossly larger, heavier oysters in areas that had never been oyster habitat, smack dab on top of shrimp habitat? And then, further amplifying the problem, by progressively adopting upland farming practices that included mowing native eelgrass, harrowing the oysters, and using large drag dredge boats to harvest the oysters—all which de-stabilized sediments?

One early indication that the shellfish companies may have caused this conflict—even before using upland farm implements in the tidelands—was evident in the late 1800s when the shellfish

---

[1] The term "chromosomally modified" as used in this book refers to the triploid oyster, an animal manipulated by humans to be sterile.

companies first laid tarpaper down on the tidelands, and then placed oysters on the paper so that they wouldn't sink. They also tried lining the ground with wooden boards—a clear indication that their growing practices were in conflict with the native shrimp long before the 1950s.

The state and shellfish companies converted shrimp habitat to non-native oyster operations at a very large scale with the help of Trevor Kincaid, a shellfish researcher and industry promoter during the late-1800s to mid-1900s. Kincaid wore many hats, including University of Washington Professor of Zoology, state consultant, and shellfish industry member. Kincaid operated the state oyster laboratory on Willapa Bay in the 1920s, is credited with establishing the Pacific oyster industry on Willapa Bay during those years, and is known as "the father of the Northwest oyster industry." Kincaid wrote in his book, *The Oyster Industry*, "It is thought that by improved methods and the utilization of land that is not as yet under tillage, that extent of the industry can be greatly increased."

In Kincaid's chronicles, he indicates that companies were spreading non-native oysters in the tideflats as if no other creatures lived in there. They considered land not under "tillage" to be vacant land. So companies spread the giant Pacific oysters further up in the intertidal zone and along shorelines that had never supported the Olympia oyster, but had likely been home to shrimp and other animals. These areas had not been oyster habitat because tidelands exposed at low tide can be very cold in winter and very hot in summer; native oysters weren't able to tolerate those temperature extremes. The temperature constraints of the Olympia oyster created natural habitat separation between the oysters and the shrimp.

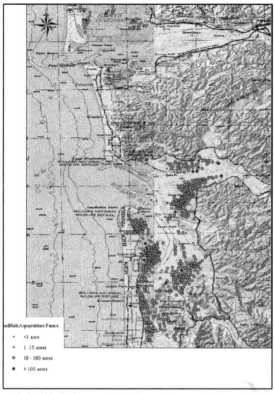

Map of shellfish farms in Willapa Bay and Grays Harbor.
(Source: US Fish & Wildlife Service)

The Pacific oyster, on the other hand, appeared to thrive both submerged in water *and* exposed during low tides. In 1941, Kincaid documented that when the shellfish companies tried to grow Olympia oysters on the tideflats, or even in shallow water, they would die from the temperature extremes. But he noted, "The Pacific oyster is, however, very resistant to both high and low temperature. Even if frozen solid they will recover if thawed out in water."

Before the shellfish companies decimated the Olympia oyster, they tried to expand its range by grading the tideflats and building a system of dikes with creosote-treated wood and concrete, holding water as much as six inches deep when the tide went out. This prevented the oysters from succumbing to the heat of summer, and the cold of winter.

The oyster growers treated tideflats as a platform for their monoculture. In Willapa Bay *and* Puget Sound, dikes were built on shrimp habitat. Under the weight of the concrete, the ground settled and the dikes cracked. The growers blamed this on the shrimp. From their perspective, the native shrimp were a "problem," so the oyster growers poisoned them. (Note: Official carbaryl use in Puget Sound ended in the 1980s, but illegal use is documented and discussed in detail in subsequent chapters of this book.)

In addition to the dramatically different temperature needs that dictate where the two oyster species could live—under water or exposed on the tideflats, how they lived was different too. The Olympia oysters grew as massive sub-tidal reefs. They didn't live on tideflats as single oysters, but that is how the shellfish companies planted their Pacific oyster seed—broadcast over the tideflats and shallow sub-tidal land as "ground culture." Not in reefs or traditional culture, but ground culture. Ground culture is single, heavy oysters lying directly on the tideflats; not attached to a reef or rock or another oyster's shell as the native oysters had done. Of all the possible oyster culture methods, this one was the most likely to create conflict with the shrimp, the same shrimp that had lived in harmony with the reef-forming native oyster for millennia.

CUT. HARROW. DREDGE.

It just so happens that mono-crop ground cultured oysters, in addition to being the method most likely to conflict with the shrimp, was ideal for mechanization. As with upland farming, mechanization reduces labor costs while greatly expanding the area that can be farmed, boosting production and profit. The shellfish companies use dredges, work boats with booms that lower large baskets made of chainmail that scrape along the bottom, stirring up sediments and sieving out the oysters, which are then hoisted aboard and emptied onto the boat deck. These drag dredges operate year-round, in almost any weather, and in shallow water.

"We wouldn't be here today if we didn't have the highest water quality."
Quote from *Willapa Bay Oysters* documentary.

Oyster harvest dredge causing turbidity.
(Source: US Fish & Wildlife Service)

"The power dredges started ... I think around 1934," Richard Murakami recalled in his Washington State oral history interview. But the dredge caused high mortality if the oysters were somewhat buried in the sediments. "What does a lot of damage is when the oysters are buried, partly buried, and the dredge bag goes over and it will just sever those oysters, break those oysters."

So in the 1940s, the shellfish companies started to harrow the tidelands and sub-tidal lands with an English harrow to pull the oysters up out of the sediments, and then they would dredge.

The harrows and the heavy dredge baskets that were dragged on the sediments caused underwater dust storms as the aquatic vegetation, especially eelgrass, was stripped out. Eelgrass roots stabilize the sediments, helping to keep the ground firm. Quite possibly, the shellfish companies were creating perfect shrimp habitat.

"We do have these seaweeds, you know, that we cut with a grass cutter, because it interferes with the feeding of the oysters. So we cut those," Richard Murakami recalled for the historical record. "Eelgrass is what it's called: eelgrass. It interferes with the oyster feeding and the oysters don't fatten up, also … it interferes with the dredging, so we cut those prior to dredging. You drag these grass cutters, a V-shaped cutter, and you drag it behind the boat and that cuts the grass, and the grass floats away."

> Just like prepping an upland farm by removing the existing vegetation, tilling, planting, and then harvesting, the tidelands were shorn of their native eelgrass starting in the 1920s. They were dredged starting in the 1930s. They were harrowed starting in the 1940s. Then, in the 1950s, the shellfish companies claimed that they started to have problems with loose sediment and blamed it on the native shrimp.

Could it be that the extensive expansion of oyster beds in the 1950s, and their mechanical harvest practices that soften the sediments and remove the stabilizing eelgrasses by mowing, harrowing, and dredging were softening the sediments and adversely impacting the shrimp and other native species? Were these transplanted upland farming practices the real problem?

But the shellfish companies blamed the soft sediments on the shrimp and claimed that the shrimp population had exploded during an El Niño event in 1957 to 1958. They claimed this overpopulation had become a problem for them. They made this same claim in subsequent years to justify spraying more and more acreage. There was a sudden overpopulation of native shrimp and the shrimp were "infesting" the bays.

INVADER

On the other hand, the Pacific oyster IS the oyster of choice for aquatic farming and is globally one of the largest introduced species of farmed shellfish. It has been farmed more than any other species of fish, mollusk, or crustacean. Worldwide production of the Pacific oyster continues to expand steadily and dominate the global shellfish aquaculture industry.

The same attributes that make the Pacific oyster an excellent farm animal also make it an excellent invasive species. Of all the oysters used in aquaculture, the Pacific oyster is arguably the most aggressive invader. In the parlance of marine biology, it is called a marine bioinvader (sort of like the marine equivalent of the starling).

The Pacific oyster has been introduced to every continent except Antarctica, and has established feral populations in all major oceans and seas. It is one of the most notorious nuisance species introduced in marine waters, and is one of the hundred worst global invaders everywhere. The Pacific oyster is recognized as the ultimate ecosystem engineer—a species that can cause a wide variety of impacts on existing communities of plants and animals wherever it is introduced.

Ecosystem engineers modify the physical environment by their presence or activities, which then have large impacts on other organisms in that system and on system interactions and processes.

For example, by blanketing hard substrates, the oysters can overgrow native species of algae and immobile invertebrates (which happened in the Wadden Sea off the Netherland coast where the oyster blanketed native mussels and the damage was considered irreversible.)

The introduction of non-native species is considered one of the greatest threats to natural biodiversity worldwide, including in marine communities. As the Pacific oyster spreads globally, modifying its environment wherever it goes because it is such a powerful ecosystem engineer, will marine plants and animals everywhere start to look the same, like the malls of America with the same stores and the same products made in the same countries?

Government reactions to the spread of the invasive Pacific oyster vary along a spectrum of management responses bounded on either end by dramatically different strategies.

On one end of the management spectrum, some governments want to eradicate the Pacific oyster from their waters, declaring it noxious and its culture illegal. In the middle, governments monitor and manage the alien oyster to—hopefully—contain it and its impacts. On the opposite end of the spectrum, governments encourage its presence as a farmed animal, generating money for local, regional, and state economies.

Washington State has taken this one step further. Washington State's response has been to poison native species that threaten or interfere with the politically influential aquaculture industry.

CHAPTER 4: CARBARYL

The war on shrimp began in 1963 when the Washington State Legislature directed the then-called Department of Fisheries (Fisheries) to arm the shellfish industry against the native shrimp. Before Fisheries settled on the first pesticide, carbaryl, they conducted a variety of pesticide experiments in Quilcene Bay on Hood Canal where shellfish companies were also inconvenienced by both species of native shrimp. Ultimately, they chose carbaryl.

In spite of their own studies that found carbaryl acutely toxic to non-target species in an area eight times the size of the directly sprayed plot, the Department of Agriculture (Agriculture) gave the nod to Fisheries to issue a pesticide permit. The shellfish companies started large-scale carbaryl spraying in 1963 on Willapa Bay and Grays Harbor, long before laws were adopted to protect the environment.

The shellfish companies, facilitated by the state, sprayed carbaryl on hundreds of acres of tideflats at low tide using helicopters outfitted with tanks and spray nozzles. They also used carbaryl powder mixed with water and sprayed it by hand. When the tide returned, those hundreds of acres became thousands as the pesticide spread off-site, still at killing levels for shrimp and many other species.

Without an understanding of the shrimp as a native species, or acknowledgement of the conversion of native shrimp habitat to non-native oyster habitat, the state and shellfish companies started killing the shrimp, because, according to Fisheries:

> The expanded burrowing shrimp population threatens the multi-million dollar oyster culture industry in the bays with reduced production.

So what is carbaryl and what's so bad about it?

Carbaryl is a potent biological agent that belongs to a class of chemicals called carbamates. Carbamates are nerve agents: they disrupt the mechanism by which nerves transmit messages to organs, and they are neurotoxins because they are poisonous and destructive to nerve tissue and cause destructive changes in the functional state of an organism. Carbamates, and another class of chemicals called organophosphorus compounds, are cholinesterase inhibitors whose primary toxic effect is to block the action of the enzyme responsible for the breakdown of the neurotransmitter: acetylcholine.

The only thing that separates the method of attack on the nervous system of carbamates from the nerve agents used in chemical warfare's organophosphorus compounds is the duration of their lock on the targeted enzyme. Carbaryl's effects are considered reversible because carbamate doesn't bind irreversibly to the target enzyme in the body, and it will eventually break down. In the meantime, death can and does occur at the right dose.[2]

Groups that work to prepare for chemical warfare recognize

---

[2] In 2001, a pesticide reform group extrapolated dosage that could kill a rat to the average human (at that time about 150 lbs.) and concluded a fatal human dose would be 2/3 of an ounce.

carbaryl as a pesticide that could be used in chemical warfare. The U.S. Centers for Disease Control includes both organophosphates and carbamates in their warfare nerve agent emergency preparedness planning since both are cholinesterase inhibitors, and either can cause mass casualties.

Cholinesterase inhibitors kill by blocking acetylcholine, the enzyme that allows muscles, glands, and organs to relax after stimulation. So, just the opposite occurs: neurotransmitter hyperactivity. Muscles, glands, and organs are continuously stimulated, which leads to uncontrolled, rapid movement of muscles, paralysis, convulsions, and death, usually caused by respiratory failure.

Tearing, eye pain, loss of muscle coordination, slurring of speech, twitching of muscles, difficulty in breathing, excessive secretions of saliva and respiratory tract mucus, mouth and nose frothing, random jerky movements, incontinence, convulsions, seizures, and coma result depending on the amount of exposure. Death is primarily due to respiratory arrest, paralysis of the respiratory muscles, intense bronchoconstriction, or all three.

SHELLFISH INDUSTRY PUBLIC SUBSIDIES

Shellfish is big business in Washington State due to one of the nation's largest and most unusual transfers of publicly owned tidelands—to private interests—at rock bottom prices, and on-going public subsidies.

When Washington entered the federal union in 1889, certain public rights associated with navigable waters were transferred from the federal government to the state, and were to be retained in public trust for the citizens of the state. These rights constitute certain enforceable public ownership and property interests according to a common law doctrine of property, known as the Public Trust Doctrine. This doctrine holds that lands between the tides and under navigable waters are inalienably dedicated to public use. The waters are to be protected from encroachments that do not serve the public's interests. Washington also chose to enter the federal union as a "nonriparian" state, meaning that upland owners who wished to have the exclusive use of adjacent riparian property would first need to obtain authorization, such as a lease, from the state.

Nonetheless, in 1890, during the very first session of the state legislature, the pioneer legislators passed the Callow Act to facilitate the development of a commercial oyster industry. This act allowed the sale of any state-owned tidelands supporting natural oyster beds to private citizens. In 1895, the Bush Act expanded the scope of saleable tidelands to include any grounds, whether or not they currently supported oyster cultivation. The Bush Act also allowed owners to cancel a deed and claim a different parcel of tideland if the originally purchased tideland proved unsuitable for oyster cultivation, an explicit acknowledgement that oyster farming was expanding into areas not naturally supportive of oysters, and into habitat occupied by other native animals, including shrimp.

The state used the tideland sale proceeds (the people's assets) to support the expense of operating the state government. Financing for Seattle's one-time Alaska Yukon-Pacific Exposition in 1907, for example, was accomplished through the sale of Lake Washington and Lake Union tidelands. The land is still there, no longer public, and the Exposition is but a faded memory.

The state politicians sold the public's tidelands—almost 45,000 acres—to private citizens for commercial oyster and clam farming upon request until the 1970s. By 1979, only 39 percent of the state's tidelands remained in public ownership, which constituted ten percent of all productive shellfish lands in the state. No other state has allowed such extensive private ownership of tidelands. Local historian, Sydney Stevens, wrote in her book, *O is for Oysters,*

"Visitors to our area are often amazed to learn that most of the tideflats of Willapa Bay are privately owned."

Then, the state decided to lease the remaining 10 percent of public tidelands conducive to non-native oyster farming to shellfish companies on Willapa Bay and Grays Harbor, with an apparent substantial annual subsidy with below fair market rents that don't even cover the cost of the state's leasing program.

DNR, the state's tideland manager, estimates the value of the annual unclaimed rents somewhere around $2,500,000. The uncertainty is due to lack of information to the DNR for the value of the oysters harvested, since the lease rate is based on a low flat rent regardless of the value of what is produced on those lands.

However, leases between private tideland owners and shellfish companies almost exclusively use a dramatically higher production rent. In these private leases, the landowner receives an agreed upon percentage of the value of the harvest, not just a flat rent based on acreage alone. And a majority of state tenants on Willapa Bay and Grays Harbor participated in the annual carbaryl spraying (permitted from 1963-2013)—with no oversight from DNR, or even knowledge of which parcels were sprayed and when.

In 1902, the state withheld selling a fraction of the public sub-tidal and inter-tidal land ... but not for use by the general public. The state kept some land to serve as an oyster nursery for the shellfish companies. Their plan was to sell using a bidding process that was ultimately overseen by a committee comprised of company representatives. Funds from these sales are managed by the committee and ploughed back into projects that benefit their industry. These lands are called Oyster Reserves, where Fisheries (renamed the Department of Fish and Wildlife (DFW) in 1994) maintains a ready supply of oyster seed. These lands are not accessible to the public, nor are the oysters available for public harvest. "It's an oyster reserve. It was set up as a seed source for the oyster growers," said John Herrold of Herrold Fish and Oysters, in *Willapa Bay Oysters*.

As *Willapa Bay Oysters* narrator Glenn Johnson explained, "The growers who have depleted their previous crop rotations of natural-set oysters on the tidelands, which they personally own, are now reaching into the state-owned Oyster Reserves, where in some cases the oysters have not been picked for fifteen to twenty years."

Even these reserves have been sprayed with carbaryl, not by the shellfish companies, but by the state.

As if the land subsidy wasn't enough to create a wealthy and powerful industry, the state grants on-going subsidies. The State Legislature extended public subsidies to industry operations by passing a law requiring Fisheries to supervise and regulate the control and treatment of pests on oyster lands.

The state funds two shellfish labs for the advancement of the oyster industry to advance hatchery technology, the study of breeding, diseases, genetic modification, and interference from other species, including native species like starfish, crabs, birds ... and shrimp.

The list goes on. Commercial shellfish companies are not required to secure a fisheries permit for their in-water facilities, whereas anyone else building a dock, ramp, or pile driving, for example, must secure a permit. According to DFW: "The bottom line here is WDFW does not have the authority to regulate or monitor what shellfish growers do on their private tidelands."

Yet aquaculture does adversely impact habitat and other species. Not able to regulate aquaculture through their agency, DFW staff provided comment to Pierce County staff in 2012 hoping that the county would condition a proposed aquaculture operation with their concerns. The DFW staff noted in this email exchange with Pierce County,

Aquaculture can change habitats from mudflats to gravel, adding aquaculture gear changes the habitat complexities and may displace some fish while attracting others. For example, clam tubes tend to displace flat fish and increase crab presence and predators that could impact juvenile salmonids. Finally, once an aquaculture facility is started, it has very little regulation form (sic) Washington DFW and other regulatory agencies. Habitat can be changed, eliminated, and **chemicals applied** for without controls. *(Emphasis added)*

And finally, there are the tax exemptions. Taxes NOT paid by the shellfish industry: 1) No sales tax on exported shellfish products or shellfish sold outside of the state; 2) No export tax; 3) No enhanced shellfish tax (excise tax) on shellfish grown from seed by the grower; 4) No Business and Occupational Tax on unprocessed shellfish that are exported; and 5) Some question whether tideland acres are assessed at their true value resulting in minimal property tax, for example, in Mason County tideland acreage netting over $1 million in revenue every five years pays only $3 per acre per year in property taxes.

CHAPTER 5: NEWCOMER

In 1983, Larry Warnberg sailed into Willapa Bay in a World War II lifeboat he had converted into a sailboat, and dropped anchor. He thought Willapa Bay was beautiful. There was something primeval about the place, with its crooked and bent trees dripping with moss, its abundant sloughs and drainages, its many birds and glimpses of grazing elk and, now and then, a black bear. Some days Larry half-expected a dinosaur to come walking out of the forest at the edge of the bay: it was that wild and elemental. Larry needed a breath of fresh air and Willapa Bay was it.

When he arrived, he knew little to nothing about the long history of the Willapa Bay shellfish industry, now in its hundred-some-odd years. (This history includes the decimation of the native Olympia oyster; introduction of the invasive non-native Pacific oyster and other species including the grass spartina; shellfish company practices that create bay-wide disturbances, including the on-going expansion of Pacific oysters throughout the bay; harrowing; cutting eelgrass; drag dredging for oysters; the annual chemical assault on the bay with carbaryl, which readily killed millions of uncounted animals, and unstudied sub-lethal impacts on birds—begun in 1963 and sprayed annually since then with public subsidy; and a profound lack of understanding as to what this was doing to the ecosystem.)

The idealistic, young Larry Warnberg was in for a big surprise. His role in this story looms large. Larry still lives in the Willapa Bay area and to this day, he has worked tirelessly to end the shellfish companies' use of the pesticides carbaryl, imazamox, imidacloprid, and the pesticides used to knock back the industry-introduced grass spartina with glyphosate, imazapyr, and the toxic surfactants discussed in a subsequent chapter.

This chapter illustrates why Larry is opposed to pesticide use, and why he was motivated to operate an oyster farm without pesticides. He is one of six citizen activists featured in this book. *(Note: To distinguish the main activist characters in this book, their first names are used, whereas other characters are referred to by surname.)*

Originally from Minnesota, Larry's parents moved to Longview, Washington, not far from Willapa Bay.

Unlike the evolution of most cities throughout history, Longview was a completely planned city, down to the location of each street, sidewalk, and street name before construction began. Longview was the location of the Long-Bell Lumber Company that bought the valley and built two mills to process all the timber they were about to cut.

The city was designed and built in the 1920s, including houses for the millworkers. The houses were laid out in rows, separated by streets in the front and alleys in the back. Each house had ample room for a backyard home garden, which abutted the alley, where the Warnbergs grew their food.

The beauty of Longview was that it was nice and flat, and easy to build on. The downside was that it was a flood plain for the Columbia River, which meant water was everywhere. And so were mosquitoes. Larry remembers the thrill of riding his bike behind the government surplus jeeps as they patrolled the alleys spraying the backyard gardens with DDT for mosquito control. These trucks were a lure for children, drawn to the mysterious trucks spraying mist as they roamed the streets.

"When I was thirteen, my foot started to hurt so my parents took me to the doctor. He diagnosed malignant bone cancer. Most of my right big toe was amputated, but I lived," he said in an interview for this book. While he was recovering in the hospital, someone brought Larry a book that had a profound impact on him. That book was Rachel Carson's *Silent Spring*.

Published in 1962, the book documented the detrimental effects on the environment—especially on birds—of the indiscriminate use of pesticides, particularly DDT. Carson accused the chemical industry of spreading misinformation, and accused public officials of accepting industry claims unquestioningly. Carson didn't win any popularity contests with pesticide manufacturers.

Soon after Larry recovered, both his parents were diagnosed with cancer. Larry started to connect the dots as he learned about pesticides and their exploding use in the Columbia basin as more and more native land was converted to agriculture and tree farms. Larry was convinced he needed to get out of Longview, so he left for Portland to attend St. Francis Seminary, and graduated in 1966. He wanted to get away from the poison that was now part of the soil and in his body, and the poison that had traumatized his family.

The Vietnam War had a dramatic impact on Larry's view of the world and on his life. He opposed the war and was a critic of the politicians who supported the war, yet held their own children back from active duty where they could be injured or killed. His brother shared his views and moved to Sweden, where he still lives. Larry remained in the U.S., but was determined to not support the war. Instead, he opted for the student deferment program ... although his right toe would have disqualified him, if he had known that fact.

Larry was prime draft fodder when he graduated from the University of Washington in 1969. "When I went to the counselors at the Student Union, I told them I had lost half a big toe, but not because of cancer. Their book said the whole toe must be missing for a 4-F physical deferment. I thought I had to choose between cutting off the stub of my toe or go to graduate school to keep my student deferment."

He quickly applied to the University of Hawaii and to Southern Illinois University because both had strong psychology departments, his major. Hawaii was beyond his budget, so he signed on to Southern Illinois, packed his new wife and as many wedding gifts as they could stuff into a beater VW bug, and made it to Carbondale with just enough money to rent an efficiency apartment. Then he hit the books.

Two years later, his wife had a degree in Special Education, and he had a Masters in Psychology. "Then Nixon deleted the student draft deferment for grad students, an obvious attempt to suppress anti-war protests conducted mostly by older grad students and returning disgruntled vets. We planned our exit to Canada, but first I complied with the draft order, appearing in St. Louis with a busload of overdosed students trying to beat the physical. I watched as guys tried to fail the hearing or eye exams. But the Army chaps were onto the tricks and they ran people through repeatedly until the kids gave up and passed the exam. At the end of a grueling eight-hour day, the final stop was a small room with three docs at a table and tall stacks of folders.

Sitting in skivvies on a bench with a bunch of nervous guys smelling of fear was not pleasant. Finally, my name came up. Fortunately, my mom had sent my medical records. The doc took one look, read that I had a malignant bone tumor, and said that was an automatic deferment. Half a missing toe kept me out of Vietnam and Canada. No need to flee to Canada; no need to continue in grad school; and no need to cut off the rest of my right toe!" Larry said with ironic relief.

But Larry stayed another year at Southern Illinois in doctoral studies, moved to Oklahoma City for an internship, and then was hired by Children's Memorial Hospital in Tulsa, Oklahoma, as a pediatric psychologist. He worked there four years, and researched diabetes for his Ph.D. dissertation. "That's where I saw a need to do more work on root causes of the diseases unleashed by industrialization," Larry explained. "When I sailed into Willapa Bay I was idealistic. I wanted to do something good for the environment, and I was sure that oysters were the answer. Oysters were gaining popularity as animals that could clean water, since they filtered water for their food. I had no idea about the annual carbaryl spraying, or the major role I was about to play in trying to get it stopped."

THE WORLD IS MY OYSTER

Like shrimp, oysters are invertebrates because they have no internal skeleton; instead, they have a protective shell. Oysters are mollusks, and are further described as "bivalves" since their shells are in two parts held together by soft tissue, the same as mussels, clams, and abalone. Key to the oyster's survival is the formation of its shell, which protects them from most predators.

Oysters have a three-chambered heart, blood, nerves, reproductive organs, and a digestive system including kidneys. They have gills for breathing and eating. As water is drawn across these delicate organs, they exchange oxygen and carbon dioxide, and tiny cilia hairs on the gills collect food. Oyster food is the same as shrimp food that comes from the water column or settles out on the soil, and consists of tiny plants and animals called phytoplankton and zooplankton, bacteria, and detritus. The mucus on oyster gills captures the food, which is sent to the mouth, eaten, and digested.

Bivalves are also indicators of the health of an ecosystem because they act as "bio-sinks," concentrating and retaining bio-toxins such as pesticides, PCBs, chemical waste and by-products, heavy metals, and coliform bacteria from agricultural runoff. Hence the movement to use bivalve's filtration ability to monitor overall ecosystem health, but arguably a good reason to keep them away from toxins when grown as food.

As mentioned earlier, Pacific oysters can live in both sub-tidal and intertidal water; covered with water on a high tide, or exposed on a low tide. To protect themselves from predators at low tide, they close their two-part shell using their powerful adductor muscle. When the shell is closed, moisture is retained for the animal within. It is this survival mechanism that enables shellfish companies to transport the animal long distances. To kill the oyster, a knife is inserted into the shell and the powerful adductor muscle is severed.

If an oyster can survive predators, including man, it can experience a long life, twenty years or more. Sometimes even fifty.

"I'm a farmer at heart, having grown up in Longview working on farms, and in our DDT-sprayed home garden. And I spent summers baling hay in Minnesota on the Warnberg family farms. Since the principles of oyster farming are the same as upland farming, I felt right at home. Instead of on land, it was in the water," Larry explained. Water quality was important to growing oysters, and this fit his desire to be a positive force in nature. Just before coming to Willapa Bay, Larry and his partner, Marge, gave away their autos, terminated their drivers' licenses, and moved aboard their renovated World War II lifeboat/sailboat, doing their best to reduce their carbon footprint, long before Pope Francis recommended it.

He developed a friendship with a member of one of the oldest oyster-growing families on Willapa Bay as he remodeled the man's house and worked with him on his salmon gillnetting boat. Larry was finding his new community and setting down roots in Nahcotta, on the eastern side of the Long Beach peninsula.

Larry avoided witnessing the helicopter-borne destruction of Vietnam where the U.S. sprayed Agent Orange, but he couldn't avoid it in Willapa Bay. The first time Larry saw the helicopter making repeated passes over the tidelands he was curious but didn't ask any questions. Later, when he found out from his partner what the helicopter was doing, he was stunned. Larry thought he was embarking on a wholesome new line of work, one he could feel good about. He had bought into the shellfish companies' claims that thanks to them, Willapa Bay was a pristine estuary and Larry wanted to be a part of that. "Not only did I embrace the notion of oysters providing water pollution-removing services through their filter feeding, I embraced oyster growing as good environmental stewardship, as something sustainable. Then, all I felt was that the growers were living a lie and I didn't want to be any part of it," Larry said, disappointed. Not many people knew about his brush with pesticides and cancer as a child, or about his work in Oklahoma before he came to Willapa Bay, two major influences on his view of chemicals including pesticides.

Before Larry returned to the Pacific Northwest and landed on Willapa Bay in 1983, he was working with kids dying from cancer. Lots of them. Today, with his crinkled clothing, curly gray hair, and dirt under his fingernails from gardening and running his sawmill, it's hard to imagine Larry Warnberg in an institutional setting. When he was a pediatric psychologist in the private children's hospital in Tulsa, he had worked in tandem with a social worker. "We developed a new program to counsel terminally ill children going through radiation and chemotherapy, which was new at the time," Larry said. Not a cure. A treatment.

The hospital in Tulsa was a regional hospital, serving a four-state area. The good news was that their program was so successful, they were soon flooded with referrals from other hospitals as the number of dying children grew. The bad news was, well, the number of dying children was growing.

Again, Larry started to connect the dots. "There were way too many kids suffering from terminal diseases and cancers," he recounted. Reflecting on his own childhood exposure to DDT and cancer, he looked around and saw uncontrolled agricultural pesticide use, precious metal mining, coal mining, and oil and gas drilling that can all pollute the aquifers with acid and other toxic chemicals generated by the extraction and production processes, as well as the release of air pollutants. Where was the drinking water coming from? What foods were the children eating, and what pesticides were used to produce them? What was in the air they breathed?

Just as Larry had left Longview, Washington, he now left Tulsa, Oklahoma. It was time for him to move on. The tragedy of watching young children suffer and then die, and a divorce, prompted him to return to Washington State.

~

Larry's partner wasn't ready to call out his extended family on the widespread carbaryl use. And as the new kid on the block, Larry wasn't either. Not yet.

CHAPTER 6: CHEMICAL WARFARE

B y the 1980s, the state and industry war on shrimp had been going on for over two decades. The native shrimp, a keystone species that had flourished in the Willapa Bay ecosystem since before the last ice age, were defenseless against it.

"It should be a message to the people that you're a much better steward of your land when you own it." Quote from *Willapa Bay Oysters* documentary.

Helicopter spraying carbaryl on oysters grown in suspended method called long line. (Source: Ecology)

By 1981, about 30,000 pounds of carbaryl had been sprayed into Willapa Bay and Grays Harbor, but their annual carbaryl-spraying program was drawing attention. Most people think that the EPA was formed to protect the environment, but it was also authorized to suspend protection to allow pesticide use.

The EPA then delegated this authority to Agriculture. Agriculture, in turn, delegated its authority to Fisheries, which then granted an annual permit to the shellfish companies, now organized as the Willapa/Grays Harbor Oyster Growers Association (Shellfish Association). That year, 1981, Ecology announced it would also require one of its own water pollution permits, harmlessly coined Water Quality Modification permits. And the spraying continued.

About 95 percent of the oyster growers in these bays belong to the Shellfish Association, with membership numbering around two dozen. Fisheries annually declared that there were no significant impacts from the spraying, even though each spraying killed over 10 million aquatic animals, with no testing or long-term monitoring of birds. The Fisheries permit was now coupled with an Ecology permit to allow the inundation of the bays with the pesticide carbaryl. They were all set. Except for that niggling opposition.

The shellfish companies and the state were deploying a neurotoxic pesticide with significant impacts across a wide range of species into two biologically significant coastal water bodies. The controversy was not going to go away.

Carbaryl "applications" resulted in massive, wide-scale mortality, including for crab. And the city of Westport, located at the mouth of Grays Harbor, was home to one of the largest crab fisheries on the West Coast. This other major fishery was politically hard to ignore, especially because the crab fisherman could see that carbaryl was killing their prey. Not only were the crabbers upset with the massive crab fatalities, they were concerned about the uptake of carbaryl in the surviving crab that they took to market, since the pesticide spread in the bays mainly killed the smaller crabs, not the adults they harvested.

"I believe that it really makes a difference in that we are a little bit more motivated to work the ground and A LOT more motivated to take care of the ground because it's ours, we own it, so it instills a sense of pride." *Willapa Bay Oysters* documentary.

Dead or alive? Dungeness crab surrounded by poison water (the carbaryl is white). An estimated 4M native Dungeness crab were killed each year when 800 acres were sprayed. Baby crab were most susceptible to mortality, adults less so, and harvest of adults was not suspended during the spraying, or afterwards. This photo also illustrates how important eelgrass is for crab cover. (Source: Ecology)

Finally, twenty years into the carbaryl-spraying program, right after the 1983 summer spraying, Ecology and Fisheries decided that an environmental analysis was required by a 1971 state law to address increasing concerns. The carbaryl proponent, the Shellfish Association, prepared the environmental analysis. One of its members was a principal author.

The introductory language of the carbaryl environmental analysis lays the foundation for its outcome, "Control of these shrimp is of significant benefit to the oyster industry: a worst case scenario, oyster growers estimate that production would be reduced by 70 to 80 percent without control of burrowing shrimp. This would represent a $5 million annual loss to the economies of Pacific and Grays Harbor counties."

The actual carbaryl spraying continued while the "proposed" spraying was being evaluated for its adverse environmental impacts. Harmonizing as a chorus, the shellfish companies, and the state claimed there were just too many native shrimp ... the shrimp that had lived in this ecosystem for millennia. And while the analysis was underway, the state allowed them to *increase* the acreage sprayed, to even more than what they were evaluating, and to spray directly onto existing beds of oysters.

Through the carbaryl mist, an analysis emerged, written by the Shellfish Association. A draft was issued in June 1984, and the final report, issued in June 1985, was accepted by the state.

Maybe it's the cover of the carbaryl final analysis: a gruesome outline of a shrimp overlaid onto Willapa Bay and Grays Harbor, like a poster for a horror movie. Or the pervasive use of the term "infestation of shrimp." Or the repetitive argument that the native shrimp should be removed (here since the Pleistocene Era, if not sooner), and replaced with the commercially valuable non-native oysters.

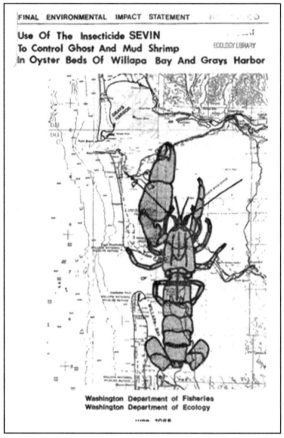

Cover of the 1985 final Environmental Impact Statement for carbaryl.
(Source: Ecology)

The native shrimp were portrayed as an evil animal, out of control, invasive, diabolical in its burrowing, and casting silt on the non-native oysters, which was causing the oysters to sink and suffocate.

Tideland where the shrimp lived was characterized as wasteland, low in biological diversity and bordering on vacant, even barren. The shrimp had to be controlled. Their presence was an "economic problem." The spraying was called the Shrimp Control Program and the applications of carbaryl to the estuarine waters were considered "treatments." The non-native Pacific oyster, on the other hand, a boon to the shellfish companies with secondary economic benefits to the region, was above the fray. It was the engine that fueled the economy, even more so than crab or salmon. Even though the crab and salmon industries were also very big business.

The state agencies received ten comment letters concerning the Shellfish Association's draft. Several letters alleged bias, omission of pertinent facts and a heavy "… reliance upon personal testimony by permit applicants and others with a vested interest in the practice of spraying. There is also an excessive reliance upon subjective observations."

One scathing letter was from none other than the National Marine Fisheries Service (NMFS), responsible for protecting marine species from extinction. NMFS pointed out that much of the information in the environmental analysis was **subjective** and that it came from industry supporters. Friends of the Earth raised similar concerns:

> The writing is poor and the statement is hampered by a lack
> of information on key subjects, incomplete data, and
> **erroneous conclusions** drawn from the evidence presented
> (*emphasis added*).

They also accused the authors of **attempting to confuse the reader**.

~

Although the state and shellfish companies said they didn't have enough studies to make an informed decision in the analysis, they went ahead and approved the pesticide use anyway:

No significant, long-term, adverse impacts have been

identified. However, additional studies are needed to better identify and quantify the extent and nature of the impacts and to assure that they are minimized as much as possible... The extent of mortalities is not known. These are unavoidable impacts that will be studied.

Fisheries and Ecology blessed the environmental analysis and approved continued spraying, and promised to conduct a long list of studies to fill the wide gaps in information they lacked when making their decision, including a study to confirm the Shellfish Association assertion that the elimination of shrimp would improve overall species abundance and diversity.

Lacking an accurate disclosure of actual and likely impacts, the state agencies declared that there was really only one major impact and that was to the Dungeness crab—second only to oysters in commercial value in Willapa Bay. To solve this problem, they proposed an "acceptable" number of crabs that could be killed, based on an estimate of how many crab they thought actually were killed.

KILL QUOTA

So a kill quota was set for Dungeness crab and a system was developed that did *not* count crab.

Instead, individual baby and juvenile crab were discounted by what their equivalent would be as legal "adult" crab when harvestable and commercially valuable. Their lives were tallied as follows: ten babies equaled one adult; three juveniles equaled one adult. The quota was then set at 12,000 adult crab, or 29 per acre. Somewhat confusing, the reality was that the number of crab actually killed could be vastly more crab depending on whether they were babies or juveniles. In addition to the manipulated mortality numbers, the kill quota did not include off-site mortalities, even though it was well known that the poison spread in the bays; an area that was never mapped or quantified by Fisheries, and then Ecology. And young crabs are far more susceptible to the drifting neurotoxin (in terms of mg carbaryl/kg of body weight) than adult crabs.

A subsequent study in 1989, one of the studies they lacked in 1985, found that the number of crab mortalities were grossly under estimated by a factor of 6 to 40, and perhaps even higher. The kill quota had been set assuming that only 400 acres would be sprayed, which was often exceeded, and then dramatically expanded to 800 acres. In the end, the kill quota was simply however many crab were killed from the direct and indirect spraying of carbaryl into these bays. The total crab kill was estimated to be around 4,000,000 per year, nearly the same as the number of shrimp (a number that is obfuscated in state environmental documents).

Yet one important fact did not surface in the decision to allow enormous crab mortalities: the native crab are considered pests by non-native monoculture shellfish companies because they can consume six to ten juvenile Pacific oysters per day.

As the state and shellfish companies walked away from this first environmental analysis of 1985, they concluded that the only short-term impacts were immediate acute toxicity. Their long-term changes were the removal of shrimp to accommodate the planting of oysters....

CHAPTER 7: LARRY KEEPS TRYING

As the new kid on the block, Larry Warnberg wasn't ready to call out his fellow shellfish growers on their widespread carbaryl use and neither was his partner, a member of an oyster-growing clan.

But they both wanted to farm oysters organically—or at least as organically as they could. Given their circumstances, they decided to take on the carbaryl issue indirectly with what they thought was a positive approach: demonstrating that oysters could be farmed successfully without pesticides.

Larry's partner owned tideland acreage in front of his house in Nahcotta and they decided that was a suitable place to run their experiment to raise oysters suspended in the water. Their plan was to use a system of stakes and lines, not as ground culture, which would avoid the conflict between the oyster and the shrimp, and the unspoken, but potentially more serious conflict with the native crabs that predate juvenile oysters growing directly on the tideflats. And it worked.

They formed a partnership to find an economical way to grow oysters without using carbaryl and to demonstrate non-pesticide farming methods. Larry's partner provided the land and cash for oyster larvae and staking material and they used his old garage as a shop for tools and material, and they planted their first crop of oysters. The real beauty of suspended lines was that they could harvest the oysters by boat on the high tide simply by pulling the lines into the boat. But over time, they found that the larvae attached to the line and separated the threads, and when there was ice on the bay, it got caught in the lines. So they dropped the use of lines and left just stakes out there to catch the naturally spawning larvae—just stakes, poked into the sediment and re-staked if they fell over. They harvested the oysters from the stakes on low tides.

This worked really well because the oysters suspended in the water grew faster than oysters placed on the ground, and their meat was considered higher quality. But most importantly, the off-bottom culture of oysters avoided predation because the crab couldn't easily get to the oysters, and the PVC pipe stakes held the oysters without sinking. *No pesticides were necessary.*

Larry Warnberg tending to his stakes. (Provided by Larry Warnberg)

Although crab predation of oysters wasn't talked about as the goal of the carbaryl-spraying program, Larry observed that, "two birds could be killed with one stone."

He also found that the ground could become soft from burrowing polycheate worms, and that there was really no way to distinguish between a shrimp burrow hole and a wormhole. Carbaryl killed the worms too, and, like the shrimp, they had long been part of the ecosystem. So, three birds could be killed with one stone: Shrimp. Crabs. and Worms.

Every summer, the partners watched the spewing helicopter, knowing that the carbaryl spray was indiscriminate and killed invertebrates and vertebrates, first on the sites sprayed and then in other parts of the bay. However, they labored on for several years, and found a ready market at local gourmet restaurants, a roadside stand, and with U-pick customers. Business was good. But growing oysters using a sustainable approach was not embraced by the bigger companies.

Larry believed the other growers were just too committed to ground culture and had too much capital tied up in laborsaving mechanical dredge harvesting. They found a few supporters among individuals who owned small tideland plots, like Fritzi and Edward Cohen, and a handful of other people who would go on to form the Ad Hoc Coalition for Willapa Bay, organized to try to keep toxic chemicals out of the water. Not only was their successful non-pesticide farming technique *not* embraced by the big companies, the area directly sprayed with carbaryl was about to be officially doubled from the 400 acre limit—to 800 acres.

1992 ENVIRONMENTAL ANALYSIS

After the first environmental analysis was issued in 1985, acknowledged by the state agencies as incomplete with missing fundamental information, the state went to work to backfill the information gaps, using state employees, University of Washington contract personnel, and other consultants to conduct the missing studies.

The results of the studies conducted between 1986 and 1990 are sobering: Carbaryl could be carried off treated "beds" by the incoming tide. Shrimp and "other invertebrates" were found dead 700 feet off the sprayed site. Carbaryl was found in the water column up to 1,700 feet from where it was sprayed. And, carbaryl could persist in the sediments, depending on conditions, for up to a year. (Persistence is a term applied to compounds that have lingering toxicity, which can be transmitted from treatment areas and possibly throughout the entire food chain.)

The breathtaking study results continued to roll in. Based on an 800-acre spray program, a staggering 4,490,400 burrowing shrimp were killed; 1,140,000 nereid worms; 284,800 Crangon shrimp (the most important prey for Dungeness crabs); 80,800 Scale worms; and 6,400 Nemertina (a type of worm). The agencies matter-of-factly stated that these numbers were likely on the *low* side because this reflected only dead animals counted immediately on the surface after spraying, and did not include animals killed off site … or over time.

The studies were summarized in a second environmental analysis, of which there was a draft that was prepared by the Shellfish Association in 1989[3], and a final.

In this document, the total estimated number of annual crab mortalities requires the reader to complete the math. A formula is given, but not totaled.

---

[3] The Shellfish Association's 1989 draft was soundly rejected by Fisheries due to bias and misrepresentation of facts, among other serious concerns (Agriculture thought it was just fine), and even though the state re-wrote the document, the outcome was the same: continued spraying.

Completing the calculation reveals that the University of Washington researchers estimated annual Willapa Bay and Grays Harbor mortalities of Dungeness crab at **1.88 million** to **4 million**. These crab mortalities are not summed up in the document, nor is there a discussion of the high predation of oysters by these same crab.

"I think we're a real benefit. I don't like this...people downgrading the business because without us this place would be a lot different. I don't think we've got anything to be ashamed of. As a matter of fact, I think we need a pat on the back." Quote in *Willapa Bay Oysters,* in reference to Willapa Bay shellfish business environmental record.

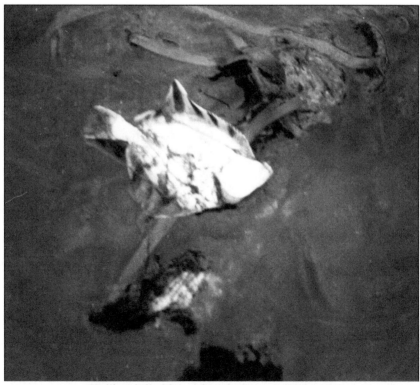

Halibut killed by carbaryl. (Source: Ecology)

Not only is the full impact of carbaryl on crab not tallied, the authors instead argued that killing crab is good for crab:

> ...the replacement of burrowing shrimp beds with areas of oysters provides young crabs with high quality rearing habitat. Because this habitat serves to shelter the young crab from predators and rigorous physical conditions, it increases the probability that more crab will survive to enter the fishery than would occur on high-density burrowing shrimp or eelgrass grounds (i.e., if the oyster shell was not there).

In any event, "killing crab was good for crab" became the response the shellfish companies and the state gave anytime someone complained about the tremendous Dungeness crab mortalities. Indeed, the ultimate conclusion was that **replacing the native shrimp with non-native oysters mitigated the impacts of the carbaryl.**

Meanwhile, the mortalities in the studies went on: Saddleback Gunnels: 158,400. Staghorn Sculpin, a shrimp predator: 116,800. Bay Gobies, which share the shrimp's burrow: 100,000. Three-spined Sticklebacks: 12,800. Starry Flounder: 3,200. And that's as far as they got. Shiner perch and blennies were killed, but not quantified.

Aquatic animals killed off site: *not quantified,* even though they knew carbaryl was toxic well beyond the area of the original sprayed site. Sub-lethal effects that might result in mortalities, deformities, or defects: not studied.

And yet again, the analysis listed all of these estimated animal mortalities, but stopped short of adding them up.

So here are tallies:

4,490,400	Burrowing shrimp
4,000,500	Dungeness crab
1,140,000	Nereid worms
284,800	Crangon shrimp

80,800	Scale worms
6,400	Nemertina (a type of worm)
158,400	Saddleback gunnels
116,800	Staghorn sculpin
100,000	Bay gobies
12,800	Three-spined sticklebacks
3,200	Starry flounder
TOTAL: 10,168,600	**Aquatic animals killed annually.**

More than 10 million aquatic animals killed annually ... and this was on the *low side* ... according to the state. The number did not include the millions, maybe billions, of tiny crustaceans that float in the water known as zooplankton (amphipods, copepods, mysis, isopods, decapods), which are at the bottom of the marine food chain.

(The state said in its analysis that out of all finfish species, salmon were the most sensitive to carbaryl and that it killed a significant salmon food source: zooplankton and ghost shrimp larvae. Over the years that carbaryl was sprayed, native salmon species declined. In 2009, NMFS determined that several threatened salmon species were present in Willapa Bay and Grays Harbor, and that they were exposed to peak carbaryl concentrations in the water column and from contaminated prey. Even with this information in hand, the state and federal agencies continued to allow salmon-killing pesticides to be sprayed into their habitat—for the benefit of a non-native shellfish industry.)

According to the Environmental Protection Agency (EPA), the carbaryl is not acutely toxic to birds, however chronic exposure to carbaryl results in "adverse reproductive effects, including decreased number of eggs produced, increased number of broken eggs, and decreased fertility." The American Bird Conservancy (ABC, and they do what their name says—conserve native birds and their habitat) disagrees that carbaryl is not acutely toxic to birds, and wrote (in

2001) to the EPA that they had evidence that it is, based on reports involving blackbirds and a dove.

The ABC told EPA that "...though relatively few incidents involving carbaryl have formally been reported to ABC or EPA, the absence of incident reports cannot be construed as the absence of incidents. Poisoned birds may fly far from the site of pesticide application before succumbing to the chemical. Dead birds are often consumed by scavengers before they are picked up by managers or concerned citizens."

In fact, concerns about disappearing birds had been raised with the state around this time. Residents in the Bruceport area of Willapa Bay reported to Ecology that they witnessed the disappearance of small bird species after several years of carbaryl spraying. Some birds returned approximately four years later, during a period when that particular area was not sprayed. The birds disappeared again when spraying resumed in that vicinity. But no rigorous studies were conducted on birds by the state or industry.

But in this 1992 analysis, the state concluded that birds weren't harmed by eating animals that died or were dying, from carbaryl. This included Glaucous Winged and Western Gulls, Crows, Dunlins, Blackbellied Plovers, Dowitchers, Ruddy Turnstones, Whimbrels, Brown Pelicans and Caspian Terns. They then recommended a study to determine sub-lethal impacts on birds; a study that was never done.

Out of all of these animals, the state and Shellfish Association concluded that the only species of major concern was the Dungeness crab because of its economic value and related political sensitivity. But even so, millions could be killed. The unspoken benefit to the shellfish companies was the elimination of a major predator of their non-native oysters: the native Dungeness crab.

Even though the studies found that 82 to 100 percent of crabs on treated "tracts" and 300 feet off tract, and crabs as far away as 600 feet from the sides of the sprayed tract would be killed, the state and Shellfish Association persisted in defining the impacted area as just the directly sprayed 800 acres. A tactic employed to this day (2018).

According to the 1992 analysis, carbaryl was found in the water column long distances from each spray site, up to 1,700 feet, yet these areas were neither quantified nor characterized. What was the total acreage impacted on Willapa Bay and Grays Harbor if not the directly sprayed 800 acres? Was it 900 acres, 3,000 acres, 5,000 acres, 10,000 acres, or maybe even 30,000 acres? And if these areas of impact *were* quantified, could the state and shellfish companies still argue, "We're just poisoning such a small fraction of each bay"?

The state declared there was no harm to humans from the carbaryl-spraying program, and that the human health risk was slight, even under the most severe exposure conditions.

"It's a damn shame and so unnecessary," said Rob Kavanaugh, a Vietnam vet, Agent Orange survivor, and active pesticide opponent not only in these bays, but throughout the state, in an interview for this book when he learned about the men who were sprayed with carbaryl *(featured in Chapter 1)*. "I'm not surprised these men have epilepsy. There may be more. Carbaryl is highly toxic. I wouldn't go anywhere near where it had been sprayed. In the Army, I was a chemical, biological, and radiological warfare officer. One of my duties was to estimate the number of casualties for certain kinds of war gas. Those are simply the kinds of things we had to do in our military planning."

Kavanaugh was in the area of the 25th Infantry Division on night reconnaissance when the Air Force flew over and sprayed powerful mixtures of herbicides to defoliate forest cover to see the Viet Cong soldiers. "I have a lot in common with Iner, Jack, and Jim," he said. "They wouldn't tell us we were going to get sprayed. The only thing we could do was to try to cover ourselves with our ponchos and move quickly. I developed all of the symptoms of Agent Orange exposure. I knew it was affecting the Vietnamese too because babies were being born with cleft palates. I knew it and so did the Air Force. Now, my liver is full of dioxin. Courtesy of the U.S. Air Force." Agent Orange contained the chemical dioxin, known to be highly toxic— even in minute doses.

Kavanaugh says he has repeatedly requested data from the Department of Health for testing of migrant workers for carbaryl. "No such data exists," he said. "They don't test for it."

"There are so many things that are trying to reach their tentacles into what we do, and there are a lot of people like to see oyster farming and any farming of the bay go away." Quote in *Willapa Bay Oysters* documentary.

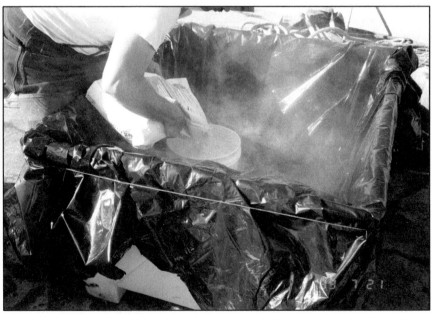

Person mixing carbaryl powder with water at one of the bulk helicopter loading stations. (Source: Ecology)

People pouring liquid carbaryl. (Source: Ecology)

This second round of study was supposed to address the gaps in missing information from the 1985 environmental analysis. But it turns out, when the state issued its final analysis in 1992, it called for yet more studies. There were still many unanswered questions. One of the studies recommended was to study the sub-lethal impacts on birds... which was never done although carbaryl spraying continued for another twenty-one years.

The larger question remained: How was the mono-crop farming of non-native oysters, and by now, the non-native manila clam, altering the habitat of these two major coastal estuaries? What would this type of farming do to the ecosystem as a whole?

To answer the broader question of the impacts of growing non-native, monoculture shellfish on the bays, they needed to understand highly complex ecosystem processes about which little was known in

Willapa Bay and Grays Harbor. But before anyone attempted to map or understand these complex systems, the state had institutionalized the poisoning of native species, disrupted the natural cycle of the entire ecosystem, and refused to stop it.

Because one thing was now certain. By their own admission, the shellfish companies were making a fortune replicating upland monoculture farming methods: reducing ecosystem complexity by poisoning, tilling, and mechanical harvesting of the non-native oysters as though they were field crops. They equated more carbaryl with more money, and argued that their use of pesticides meant jobs for the hard hit rural Pacific and Grays Harbor counties.

In a letter the Shellfish Association's attorney wrote to Fisheries in 1990, they made it clear that the more carbaryl they could use, the more money they could make.

> In 1957, a 14-acre oyster tract could not be cultured due to shrimp infestations. In 1971, this bed was treated with Sevin (the brand name for carbaryl) and in 1972, it was replanted with oysters. A second crop planted in 1976 produced 24,000 gallons of oyster meat in 1979 (worth $460,000 at current prices) … Without treatment, only 7,200 gallons of oysters would have been produced; the cost of production then would have exceeded the income.

At three critical decision points—1963, when Fisheries first allowed carbaryl; 1985, when the program was evaluated under the state's relatively new environmental laws; and 1992, with yet another incomplete environmental analysis—the state kept on approving carbaryl use. Even in the face of admittedly under-estimated but still staggering numbers of animal fatalities (10,000,000), the state wouldn't say "No."

OREGON SAYS, HELL NO!

What would it have taken for the state to stop the spraying if an admittedly under-estimated ten-plus million aquatic animals was not enough? Was there any number that could have convinced the state to stop the spraying? Instead of four million Dungeness crab, how about ten million? Were there *any* unacceptable thresholds for any species?

But maybe these are the wrong numbers.

There was a different numbers game being played out south of the Washington border. The state of Oregon wasn't subsidizing this aspect of its shellfish industry, and the use of carbaryl on the tidelands was halted. Carbaryl had been sprayed from 1964 to 1981, but was stopped by the Oregon Land Use Board of Appeals based on a petition brought by three environmental groups. The Oregon shellfish companies also argued that shrimp interfered with the ground-culture growing technique for oysters, but the Oregon Land Use Board of Appeals concluded that the Oregon Department of Fish and Wildlife had approved the use of carbaryl in error, by ignoring evidence that did not support such a decision. The Oregon Land Use Board of Appeals also dismissed studies performed in Washington State as ... unreliable. They said that Washington State's finding that organisms affected by carbaryl would "regenerate rapidly" was not supported by reliable evidence and had been made without addressing the question of how organisms outside the target area would be affected.

Since no state or private funds were available to challenge the Oregon Land Use Board of Appeals decision, or their subsequent affirmation, or to do studies designed to support the oyster farmers' arguments, the spraying was ended.

But in Washington, public funds to support the shellfish industry are readily available. The public funds a wide variety of shellfish studies, including the use of pesticides. Even Willapa Bay Oyster Reserve (public lands set aside as oyster nurseries) sales of oysters to shellfish companies, overseen by shellfish companies, are used to fund research conducted almost exclusively by WSU, UW, and the shellfish industry's own private Pacific Shellfish Institute.

One of the earliest state-subsidized efforts was to relieve the local oyster businesses from having to buy larvae each year from Japan by studying the conditions needed for the non-native Pacific oyster to colonize in Washington waters, and the creation of a public shellfish lab in Nahcotta. Public tidelands were sold to shellfish companies shortly after statehood and the practice continued until 1979. The purpose was to facilitate this industry with the result of preventing public access forever, and evidently environmental protection, since the state now says they can't regulate aquaculture in Washington's marine waters because the underlying plot of land is privately owned.

Was it difficult for the biologists to release killing levels of toxins into the environment, and then methodically document the mortalities? Was anyone fired for speaking out?

It bothered at least one young biologist, Dan Ayres, who was just beginning his Fisheries career in the 1980s. At a Fish and Wildlife Commission meeting in 2016, Ayres told the Commission that when he was a young biologist he was tasked with counting the mortalities after the spraying, and that it was highly disconcerting for him.

Another biologist worked for Fisheries during that time and had conducted some of the early studies. He went on to work for the Shellfish Association, overseeing the annual spray program, and had his own oyster farm. "Oyster growers ... very concerned with water quality. Probably the cleanest estuary in the country," he said in *Willapa Bay Oysters*. "The only other estuaries that could be any cleaner are probably in Alaska, like the mouth of the Yukon River.

Where there's not much there. The oyster growers are basically the reason why they are."

One paid researcher, now retired, was interviewed for this book and when asked about the millions of animals that died annually, counseled, "You have to understand, these mortalities are only a small fraction of the animals in the bay."

More than ten million animals.

CHAPTER 8: STONEWALLED

If you killed even one bird, salmon, or seal, this spraying would be stopped immediately, while we can kill all the crab and bottom fish we want and it seems to be all right," Ernie Summers wrote in 1991. Ernie, a reluctant member of the Burrowing Shrimp Committee, formed that year, was the Washington Dungeness Crab Fishermen's Association founder and president. "Meeting after meeting, I brought things up about crab, and most of the time they weren't even written into the minutes!" Ernie continued in full-throttle frustration, "I had to go back and coerce them into putting some details back into the minutes!"

Since Ecology and Fisheries had approved (and expanded) the controversial spraying program, the people who were vocally and passionately opposed to the spraying were pessimistic. That included Ernie Summers.

Ernie was born in Raymond, and spent his childhood in Tokeland, on Willapa Bay. His father took him fishing when he was little, and when old enough to have his own boat, Ernie bought the first of the four workboats he acquired during his lifetime. Married, he settled near Tokeland. He left Pacific County only once, to serve in the U.S. Army during the Korean War. The waters of Willapa Bay ran in his veins; it was his home. And he was as salty as they came.

BURROWING SHRIMP COMMITTEE

After the four-year process to develop the 1992 environmental analysis, Fisheries, Ecology, and Agriculture staff were under strong political pressure from local elected officials, and environmental groups to figure out a way to deal with the "carbaryl controversy." Meanwhile, the shellfish companies kept up political pressure to allow unfettered carbaryl use.

The path of least resistance was to keep approving the annual spraying, which the state agencies did, and, to kick this tar baby to a committee, which they did in 1991 on a parallel track with the environmental analysis. The purpose of the Burrowing Shrimp Committee (Committee) was to oversee the development of an Integrated Pest Management Plan (IPMP). Chris Gregoire, then Ecology Director, helped create the Committee. She later became Washington State's Attorney General, and then elected Governor. During all these years, the spraying continued under Ecology's permits, married with Agriculture's aggressive support.

"No, I will not sit on there with a bunch of oystermen," crab association member Don Stedman told Fisheries when they invited him to serve on the Burrowing Shrimp Committee.

Next, they asked Ernie. In his late 50s by then, Ernie was asked to serve on the Committee as the crab representative—the only commercial wild animal harvester represented on the committee. (Industrially farmed oysters are not considered wild animals.) Ernie told the Fisheries Deputy Director Judith Freeman, who had asked him to serve on the committee, that the crabbers wanted the spraying stopped, period.

Carbaryl was sure death for baby and juvenile crabs at the concentrations used on the burrowing shrimp, but a lot of the adult crabs could withstand those levels. There was no prohibition to harvest adult crab during, or after, the carbaryl spraying. So Ernie reluctantly agreed to serve, but he told Freeman, "I don't think it will do any good." After all, the shellfish companies had been spraying carbaryl non-stop since 1963 exclusively for their benefit. It was then 1991. For twenty-eight years, the state had allowed the inundation of these two major coastal estuaries with a neurotoxin. What could possibly stop them now?

The purpose of the IPMP was to reduce or eliminate the use of carbaryl by exploring alternative methods to control the shrimp, and finding alternative ways of growing oysters, such as the method pioneered by Larry Warnberg and his partner, but not embraced by the other companies. Alternative shrimp-control methods were to include other chemicals, biological agents, and mechanical measures.

But there were several problems with this process. First, the effort was governed by two stipulations that precluded non-chemical use. Any Committee recommendations had to be: 1) economical for the shellfish companies, and 2) had to assure that historical levels of commercial oyster production be maintained and, if possible, expanded. Agriculture imposed these constraints because they wanted the oyster industry to be able to use pesticides.

The reality was that ground culture, laying the oysters on the tideflats, had already proven unsustainable without the use of pesticides. Therefore, if the current pesticide-dependent levels of production were to be sustained, or expanded, it was unlikely that the Shellfish Association would agree to reduce pesticide use.

Second, representation on the Committee was stacked with shellfish companies or others with some form of financial reliance on the industry. Pacific and Grays Harbor counties, hard hit by the over-harvest of the forests and various fisheries, and subsequent industry contractions, were eager for jobs. State agency employees were dependent on their paychecks and not likely to jeopardize their jobs by opposing the powerful shellfish industry with its Olympia lobby and direct influence on state agency budgets. University researchers were eager to do studies that had funding support. Getting right to the point, the Shellfish Association openly said that use of carbaryl was necessary to keep these jobs: carbaryl = jobs.

Ernie pointed out in one of his many letters, "There has been no representation from the ground fish, salmon, Sierra Club, bird watchers, Friends of the Earth, Trout Unlimited, etc, on this committee. The majority of the committee is oyster-related people." State agency staff agreed with Ernie on this one. "Fisheries believes that the present committee was disproportionately influenced by the oyster industry," they wrote in a memo at that time, and, "Ecology and Fisheries believe the Burrowing Shrimp Control Committee lacks participation from environmental and fishing (other than crab fishing) interests."

Ernie Summers persisted in speaking up at the committee's table. Pigeonholed as a "small, but vocal, minority," Ernie kept raising issues about the tremendous ecosystem impacts from the spraying. "Every effort should be made to come up with a different solution than the use of … spray," he wrote in another letter. When he was accused of wanting only to protect the crab to line his own pocket, he clarified his view, "I would be opposed to the chemical even if it did not kill crabs."

Like Larry Warnberg, Ernie was an underdog fighting just one of many battles in the Shellfish Association's war against native shrimp. No one else involved on the Committee in the early 1990s was as outspoken and adamantly opposed to the spraying as he was. His legacy is evident in the record with his plainspoken memos and letters, raising the same unresolved issues over and over again.

But his thirty-plus years of experience on the waters were dismissed by the Chair of the Committee who was also an Agriculture employee, and an oyster grower who was one of the most vocal and influential proponents for the use of carbaryl. He was the same oyster grower that wrote the environmental documents in the mid-1980s and early-1990s. His style is captured by a comment on the agency's re-write of documents he co-authored—the state found them too biased. He wrote, "In general, this new, unreferenced, sophomoric section has little to do with the section as a whole. If there is a purpose, it would seem to be to promote the value of the burrowing shrimp and to suggest that carbaryl is disrupting the food web."

Ernie was deeply upset that the state agencies enabled the shellfish companies while casting him as an overly loud minority. He just wouldn't compromise and let these issues go, which he knew wasn't how one got ahead in this system. His marginalization was guaranteed. "Department's Famous Last Words," he headlined in a letter to Larry Blum, Director of Fisheries, copied to Chris Gregoire, Ecology Director, in 1991.

In that letter, Ernie articulated what he felt were broken promises: the state was allowing harm instead of protecting the environment; oyster farming was expanding into shrimp habitat; spraying had been increased; crab kill was unlimited; areas were not inspected prior to spraying, just dead crabs counted afterward; first prohibiting spraying over oysters, then allowing it; reducing the spray buffers along drainages from 300 to 200 feet; disingenuously calling the annual program an experimental spray program; promising that the spray would be phased out, but then increasing it; and ignoring the crabbers concern about crab kill from oyster dredging.

KILLING CRABS IS GOOD FOR CRABS...?

The litany of broken promises and customized studies was flabbergasting. Ernie was fed up with the repetitive oxymoronic concept that killing shrimp and crabs made good habitat for the crab.

"I get tired of hearing that spraying makes more habitat for crab. We could make habitat for crab without the spraying or killing of crab."

Killing crab to help the crab was an argument no scientist or degreed puff-bag could make fly with Ernie whether he had a college degree or not. Again and again, he assured everyone that crab habitat could be improved without spraying the bays with carbaryl. Nevertheless, the notion that crab habitat could be improved without spraying had no traction. The industry would have its way.

Ernie's lifetime of crabbing and fishing couldn't compete with the state and industry study that proved that killing the crab was better for the crab. A 1990 University of Washington (UW) study determined that the 100 percent mortality rate of Dungeness crab on carbaryl-sprayed land was simply collateral damage, and was more than mitigated by covering the poisoned tidelands with crushed oyster shells to make oyster habitat. And since small crabs could hide under oyster shells, "killing crabs was good for crabs."

This study was legitimized with UW fingerprints—it was evidently all the proof the shellfish companies needed to perpetuate their argument that carbaryl-sprayed oyster beds were better for crabs than native shrimp habitat. It was also the foundation for an emerging hypothesis: the entire ecosystem biodiversity would benefit from the removal of the native shrimp that had been present in Willapa Bay since the Pleistocene Era.

Ernie was concerned that people who bought the sprayed crab were unknowingly consuming toxins.

Originally, the EPA, Fisheries, and Ecology did not allow spraying carbaryl on oysters at all, later they allowed it but with a restriction that those oysters could not be harvested within two years of spraying. Then this restriction was reduced to one year. (Ecology, Agriculture, and the Department of Health each responded to a public records request that they did not monitor the one-year harvest restriction.) Ernie pointed out that crab were harvested daily, right through the spraying, and could have been exposed to carbaryl directly, or by consuming poisoned shrimp.

Studies done by Union Carbide, the manufacturer of carbaryl, seemed to support Ernie's concern. Union Carbide conducted chemical studies for Fisheries in 1961 and 1962 to determine carbaryl residue in animals, and found higher values of carbaryl in crab and ghost shrimp, than in oysters.

ERNIE FINALLY QUITS

After it became apparent that the Committee could not meet its charge to reduce or eliminate carbaryl use, a facilitator was brought in. It didn't help that an Agriculture employee was the Committee Chair and an advocate of pesticide use for the oyster industry. He referred to anyone who opposed pesticides as suffering from "chemophobia," as if it was a mental illness.

In addition to his slant, the Committee chair allegedly tolerated and encouraged brutal personal attacks on committee members, and engaged in intimidation tactics himself, especially against Ernie Summers. Ernie felt he was verbally abused by the shellfish companies repeatedly, with the blessing and participation of the Committee Chair.

The facilitator helped the Committee develop criteria for ranking alternatives to carbaryl use, as compared to the continued use of carbaryl. But the members did not vote based on these criteria. Fisheries staff observed that the members simply voted for their own preferences rather than objectively evaluating alternatives against these criteria.

Validating Ernie and Fisheries staff concerns, the Committee recommended a doubling of the number of acres that could be treated annually with carbaryl, plus more studies. After a year of often-contentious all-day monthly meetings, this was clearly an affront. Ernie got so mad, he walked out of the last few meetings and then quit altogether.

FISHERIES QUITS, TOO

Fisheries quit too. Mary Lou Mills, Fisheries staff, said her agency had probably done more than it should in support of the shellfish companies, a pattern that dated back to the earliest days of Fisheries' origins. "The problem now is to 'wean' the oyster industry from the support it has enjoyed, paid for by the taxpayers," she said at a 1992 inter-agency meeting discussing the Committee.

The carbaryl program was an unfunded headache for Fisheries and they wanted out. The annual program consumed staff time to conduct the pre-treatment inspections, permit writing, scheduling and coordination, spray monitoring, the counting of dead crab, and post-spray report writing. The Shellfish Association paid no fees to cover these public costs. Yet no good deed went unpunished: the shellfish companies had come to hate Fisheries because Fisheries resisted increasing the spray area from 400 acres to 1,000, acres and they weren't happy with the way Fisheries allocated those 400 acres in some years. Ticked, Fisheries told them to allocate it among themselves.

The impending merger of Fisheries and the Department of Wildlife provided the opportunity for the agency to bail, so attention turned to Ecology. But Ecology staff, already frustrated with trying to monitor the spraying, and as witness to permit violations aided by Agriculture, recommended that the program remain with Fisheries where it could be closely monitored, until it was phased out. The whole program was too political and time consuming for Ecology staff to adequately manage. Several staff members wrote plainly at the time that Ecology had limited personnel and virtually no expertise in this area.

Regardless, in September 1992, the directors of Fisheries, Ecology, and Agriculture formalized an agreement whereby Ecology would assume primary responsibility for managing the carbaryl program, as well as support the Burrowing Shrimp Committee and Integrated Pest Management Plan process—the whole kit and caboodle.

In the end, Fisheries' attempts to wean the oyster industry off public subsidy was apparently just a shift in veins.

SENATOR SID SNYDER'S 1993 MEETING

Senator Sid Snyder snapped at Fisheries staff at a public meeting he'd convened in 1993 to try to jumpstart the failed Burrowing Shrimp Committee's effort to develop an Integrated Pest Management Plan (IPMP). Fisheries staff said the carbaryl program was unfunded and low-priority and that cutting it from the agency's budget was simply a fiscal decision. Senator Snyder grilled, "You're saying this wasn't a priority with the department?" He countered that supporting the carbaryl program and the oyster industry should be considered a form of stewardship, and therefore a higher priority for Fisheries funding.

When Fisheries staff responded that stewardship of natural resources was indeed their legislative mandate, not catering to individual oyster growers, Senator Snyder ended the public discussion with, "We'll talk about that later."

The spraying continued, now under Ecology's authority, but with a major difference. When Ecology took over in 1993, they discontinued the on-the-ground supervision and monitoring of fish and wildlife impacts such as crab kill counts and bird surveys that Fisheries had provided.

Ecology's lead program staff person became a carbaryl advocate and said that there were no long-term impacts to plant or animal populations, especially to crab, since the commercial catch had not gone down.

Bill Young scoffed at his colleague, Steve Saunders, Ecology's surface and ground water quality unit supervisor in an intense email exchange where Saunders asserted that the only reason Ecology was allowing the spraying was due to political and economic pressure. Young challenged Saunders to prove any adverse impacts to either human or environmental health.

The IPMP developed by the Committee was never formally adopted by Fisheries or Ecology, although Agriculture and Pacific and Grays Harbor counties found continued spraying and the draft acceptable. For Ernie Summers, the annual spraying of carbaryl wasn't some abstract concept, easy for someone sitting in an office somewhere to forget about at the end of the day. This was Ernie's home, where he made his livelihood doing physically demanding work out on the water. It was real to him. It was explained to Ernie that this whole IPMP was a process, and not intended to cause some immediate shift.

The spraying of carbaryl wasn't amorphous for Ernie. He didn't agree that if putting toxins into the estuarine ecosystem was part of a written plan, that made it okay. He read the writing on the wall and in frustration and failing health, registered his formal protests, quit the Committee, and went on to do what he could for the region that he loved and respected.

In an interview for this book, his widow, Julie Summers, reminisced, "We decided you can't fight the government and win." She tried to help Ernie, taking pictures of vast amounts of dead crab washed up on the beach at Tokeland after spraying, but no one seemed to care.

"The bottom line was the oyster farmers had Senator Sid Snyder on their side, and he was a very powerful ally. Essentially, the oyster farmers had more political clout than the crabbers," stated Steve Saunders (the former Ecology surface and ground water quality unit supervisor) in an interview. "Another powerful player was the Washington State University Extension agent at the Long Beach field station, Kim Patten. They were not approaching this from an environmental standpoint, not like Ecology or Fisheries, but from trying to enhance aquatic farming, oysters in particular. They are good people, and I got along with them well. But we did not see eye to eye on the use of chemicals, especially in the aquatic environment. My job was to protect water quality; his job was to protect the industry."

The spraying continued. It was done every year, and expanded by Ecology to the full 800 acres "evaluated" in the 1985 and 1992 analyses as soon as they took over the program in 1993. Ecology continued to authorize the annual spraying over the next decade, but only through a narrow program regarding water quality. It did not consider impacts to sediments, or the dramatic decline of species on a path to potential extinction for cutthroat trout, sturgeon, and salmon.

Year after year, Ecology authorized the carbaryl spraying without updating either of the environmental documents, both of which Ecology admitted were compromised by the nagging lack of information.

Ten million aquatic animals were killed annually—a number that did not include all the baby and juvenile oysters killed from the carbaryl, or all the animals killed in other parts of the bays, including the microscopic zooplankton. This number did not account for mortalities from carbaryl's sub-lethal affects such as thinned shells; depressed immune responses; reproductive damages including birth defects, fetal mortality, and reduced fertility; slowed development or increased deformities—evidence that was building in laboratory and epidemiological studies.

Carbaryl was sprayed in 1992, 1993, 1994, 1995, 1996, 1997, 1998, 1999, and 2000. Over this timeframe, the local Shoalwater Bay Tribe's abnormally high rate of miscarriage, birth defects, and infant mortalities hit the national news.

CHAPTER 9: SMALLPOX INOCULATED BLANKET

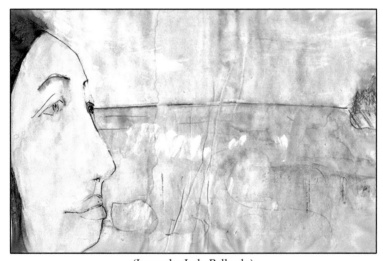

(Image by Lola Pallardy)

Something was killing the fetuses and newborns of the already tiny Shoalwater Bay Tribe.

Year after year, the Shoalwater Bay Tribe, as well as the Chinook Tribe representing other lower Columbia River tribes, had been strenuously objecting to the carbaryl spraying program and, like everyone else, were brushed off or ignored as evidenced by the continued and expanded spraying.

In 1992, the Shoalwater Bay Tribal Council declared a health emergency, pointing to a staggeringly high prenatal and neonatal infant mortality rate (before birth and shortly after). Ectopic pregnancies in the community were ten times the expected rate in Washington State, stillbirths were twenty-nine times the expected rate, and infant mortality was twenty-four times the expected rate. Only 42 percent of pregnancies produced a healthy child, compared to 82 percent for the state of Washington as a whole.

A few hundred years ago, the Shoalwater Bay Tribe once numbered in the tens of thousands. The Shoalwaters' village looks out onto Willapa Bay and an ever-shifting panorama of sand dunes, driftwood, tides, and waves. They lived along the Pacific Coast near the mouth of the Columbia, fishing the estuaries, harvesting clams from the area's shallow bays, and hunting seal and other animals. The Shoalwater were expert canoe makers. They roamed vast coastal lands, navigating the seas and inland waters in canoes carved from Western red cedar.

The Indians feasted on the abundant shellfish, and each Shoalwater member relied on a personal guardian spirit, called Tomanawas.

But in the early 1800s, Europeans infected the native North American Indians with smallpox, venereal disease, and other illnesses, and by the 1850s, only pockets of Indians survived. In 1855, the territorial government removed the Shoalwater from their traditional fishing grounds along the coast and Columbia River, and tried to force them to share a reservation with a nearby antagonistic tribe. In 1866, the Shoalwater were moved to a 1,035-acre reservation. The majority of their land *is* Willapa Bay, tidelands and wetlands, with only a few usable upland acres.

The pregnancy loss crisis was not the first time the Shoalwater had to defend their right to exist. During the 1960s, they narrowly avoided termination as a tribe by the federal government. The Shoalwater view all these experiences as part of a broader colonial narrative. The tribe was the poorest in the state—90 percent of its members lived below the poverty line.

After tribal officials sounded the alarm in 1992, national and local media picked up the story. On Tom Brokaw's *NBC Nightly News*, Herb Whitish, chairman of the 150-member tribe, said, "The tribe, and me in particular, are getting real damn tired of hearing that because we've only got 150 people, we don't count." Herb said that over the years, his tribe had lost its land, its pride, its identity. Now it was fighting for its very life. "If our people cannot keep their babies, our way of life here will die."

Tribal members lead a traditional lifestyle of subsistence fishing and harvesting, and eat a lot of fish and shellfish. They consume three to ten, sometimes even twenty times the amount of fish and shellfish the average U.S. consumers eat. Willapa Bay feeds not only the Shoalwaters, but people all over the globe who consume fish, shellfish, and crab from this once pristine bay.

The Washington Department of Health and the Portland Area Indian Health Service made a study of the tribe's health crisis to determine if environmental toxins or lack of access to medical care might be factors in the high rates of pregnancy loss on the reservation in the early 1990s. But according to Herb Whitish, "They didn't try to get questions asked. We wanted them to look at environmental issues and the Indian Health Service's lack of healthcare down in this area. There are no neonatal programs most other tribes have access to."

The tribe members felt the preliminary report blamed their health habits on pregnancy loss, and ignored possible environmental causes; the leaching and run-off from a World War I munitions dump a mile from the reservation; the chemicals used on nearby forests and in cranberry bogs; and the long-term spraying of carbaryl on shrimp habitat. In addition, the herbicide, glyphosate, was now being sprayed in Willapa Bay on the spartina *(discussed in subsequent chapters)*. "The acreage they're covering is getting larger and larger every year," said a frustrated Herb Whitish about the in-water spraying.

In addition to the annual spraying of carbaryl in Willapa Bay, and now glyphosate, commercial forests covered two-thirds of the bay's watershed and unwanted vegetation was killed using herbicides sprayed from helicopters. Cranberry bogs—1,400 acres of the bay's watershed—were sprayed from February through August with fungicides and insecticides. The Shoalwater were surrounded by chemical use, like a modern day smallpox-inoculated blanket.

Six-month-old Shoalwater John Anderson had been sickly off and on since birth. On July 5, 1993, the baby was again ill. His parents, Kathy and Jim Anderson, drove him to the emergency room in Aberdeen. The couple also had a five-year-old son, David, born before the troubles began.

"He (John) had his fingers wrapped around my finger," Kathy told a local paper. "He looked right up at me. That's when he died. We were only a few minutes from the hospital." The death was attributed to dehydration and pneumonia.

Kathy Anderson was pregnant again in November when, five weeks from her due date, she woke in the night with severe abdominal pains. An ambulance rushed her to the hospital where she underwent a Cesarean section. The baby, Fern Willi, was born dead. As a result of complications from this pregnancy, Kathy is unable to have more children.

"People were wanting to invest in this child," said a tribal administrator, speaking of Fern, in an interview with the *Los Angeles Times* in 1993. "We were thinking: Maybe this one is going to make it.

I can remember the phone call coming in that the baby had died. You could hear a ripple of sobs throughout the office."

In 1994, Herb wrote another letter to Ecology opposing the annual carbaryl spraying, and expressed frustration that tribal concerns were routinely dismissed.

EPA STUDY

After the mainstream media coverage about the high rate of reproductive problems, and the report recommending further environmental contaminant study, the EPA got involved and conducted a limited environmental assessment between 1994 and 1996.

Chuck Clarke, the EPA regional director, was a defender of the spraying when he served as Governor Gardner's politically appointed Director of Ecology, and just a few years prior, in 1992, he assured Gardner that the program was sustainable. Now he was working for EPA. He met with Herb at the Shoalwater Reservation. Clarke's visit was taken as a sign that the EPA was responsive to the tribe's concern that environmental contaminants might be adversely affecting the health of the tribal members. Clarke committed to explore the possibility that tribal exposure to various environmental contaminants in the Willapa Bay ecosystem might somehow be related to their health and reproductive problems.

The EPA study sampled oysters and clam for bacteria, but *not* pesticides. Fish weren't tested either.

Oysters, like other bivalves, are able to remove pesticides, chemical wastes, heavy metals, and fecal coliform from the water and can accumulate in the tissues of the animal, but leave it unharmed. However, these toxins can make oysters unhealthy for human consumption. Without sampling a significant known food source for the tribe—fish and shellfish—for potential pesticide contamination, the EPA concluded there was no direct link between infant mortality and environmental conditions.

The EPA study focused on four nearby exposure pathways:

1. an abandoned World War I munitions dump and later municipal dump that drained into Willapa Bay near the reservation;
2. the tideflats subject to carbaryl spraying, and now bay-wide glyphosate spraying that was ramping up to kill the invasive oyster-company introduced spartina;
3. runoff from forest lands and nearby cranberry bogs where intensive pesticide use was practiced; and
4. drinking water.

Except for drinking water, only a small number of environmental samples were taken. As for sediment samples, five were taken near the reservation at the north end of Willapa Bay as a "snapshot in time," not as a long-term study.

The report raised concerns about carbaryl drift, but not the well-documented spread of carbaryl in the water; it focused on carbaryl in the *air*. Over the years, the state departments of Agriculture, Health, and Ecology had received complaints about spray drift from tribal members and other individuals who lived in the area of human exposure.

In one instance, a woman who lived near the Reservation was so concerned about her symptoms after the aerial spraying that she went to her doctor and filed a complaint with Ecology. She was increasingly concerned when her neighbors told her they had similar symptoms. The Department of Health recommended to Ecology that every effort should be made to minimize the possibility of aerial drift. Those actions included pre-notification of neighboring properties to allow people time to avoid potential for exposure *by closing windows and doors, or leaving the house.*

According to the EPA, "The most obvious environmental problem was pesticide contamination of surface water in runoff from cranberry bogs where DDT, azinphos-methyl, chlorpyrifos, and diazinon were detected at excessive levels; levels that exceeded federal and state water quality standards." Grayland Creek discharged from the cranberry bog drainage to Willapa Bay, about a mile from the tribe's headquarters.

Did this come as a complete surprise to the state? Agriculture and WSU field offices located in Long Beach and Aberdeen facilitate the use of pesticides on cranberries and have done so since 1927, when WSU sent D.J. Crowley to Long Beach peninsula to help farmers by developing chemical sprays to rid the vines of pests and weeds. In fact, the Long Beach compound of the WSU Extension Field office is contaminated with pesticides and semi-volatile organic compounds used by the cranberry industry.

After claiming no linkage between environmental contaminants and tribal health issues, the EPA study went on to say, "Tribal concerns about the effects of pesticides and herbicides on Willapa Bay ecosystem are given credence by the findings of the report. At this time, long-term effects are unknown and further study is clearly needed." The study also said, "The possibility of chemical pollutants in the tidelands near the Reservation has long been a concern of area residents. These concerns are well founded."

Although EPA said they did not expect to find a direct link between environmental conditions and infant mortality, they did determine that risks to humans and animals during periods of pesticide application were considerable, as were risks to "non-target" species such as fish, aquatic birds, and small invertebrates.

The EPA recommended more study.

Inhalation exposure from the carbaryl spraying was not known, but there was a history of concern, so the EPA recommended air monitoring during aerial pesticide application events. Still, EPA concluded that there was no specific environmental contamination to suggest a causal or contributory relationship to the tribe's ongoing health and reproductive problems.

State and federal representatives did not identify any of the contaminant sources evaluated in the EPA study as responsible for the deaths, and the conclusion was that making such a connection would be difficult. Gary Burns, the tribe's environmental program manager at the time, said that even though studies had linked pesticides to reproductive problems in animals, it would be difficult to connect the Shoalwaters' fetal deaths with the pesticide use. "If there is an environmental link to this, we probably won't make it," Burns said.

The spraying continued throughout the entire Shoalwater baby crisis of the early 1990s.

Between 1993 and 1996, four healthy babies were born in the tribe; the baby death crisis seemed to have passed. But in 1999, fears rose again. Herb Whitish again used blunt language and media savvy to bring the Shoalwaters' difficulties to the nation's attention. This time the Centers for Disease Control (CDC) sent in an elite epidemiological team.

CDC Study

The results of CDC's study estimated that from 1988 to 1992, fifty-three percent of pregnancies on the reservation ended in miscarriage or fetal death. By 1998, eighty-nine percent of pregnancies (eight out of nine on the reservation) ended in child loss. In addition to stillbirths, infant mortality, ectopic pregnancy, and miscarriages, two women experienced molar pregnancies. This is a rare condition in which the embryo dies quickly but a group of precancerous cells continues to grow in the uterus, making the woman think she is still pregnant. The condition is so rare that having two cases in a tiny community "is clearly worrisome," said Dr. William Freeman, director of research for the Indian Health Service in Albuquerque.

"The loss of genetic material in human ova that leads to molar pregnancies could be caused by environmental factors," said Dr. Kurt Benirschke at that time. Benirschke is a nationally recognized expert on molar pregnancies and diseases of the placenta. "The real problem is to understand why there are eggs that don't have a nucleus," he said. "People have considered the possibility that this ... is an environmental feature. I think that it is a good possibility."

The CDC alluded to possible causes by making several recommendations, such as examining environmental concerns, providing optimal health care, monitoring pregnancies, and conducting health education programs to reduce behavioral risks such as consumption of alcohol and drugs. Their report concluded that there was no data to suggest that the problem was related to substance abuse.

One of the CDC's recommendations was that the tribe should evaluate any "preventable genetic or environmental components" to the miscarriage crisis. So, the tribe applied for a $600,000 grant from the federal Department of Health and Human Services to develop its own testing program for the reservation. "If there is something out there, let's find it," said Gary Burns, the tribe's environmental director. "If there isn't, let's put it to rest so people can get on with their lives."

When the Shoalwater questioned potential synergistic effects between Ecology's permitted annual carbaryl spraying, and the proposed spraying of spartina with glyphosate, then imazapyr, Bill Young responded in a letter to the Shoalwater, "While there is no definitive answer to that question, neither is there a reason to expect carbaryl, a neurotoxic insecticide ... and glyphosate ... to react in a synergistic way."

Jim Skogen, whose story was told in Chapter 1, says he was repeatedly sprayed with carbaryl. The first day he was sprayed, he had an epileptic seizure. Now, suffering from debilitating and chronic epilepsy, he has an uphill battle to prove that acute exposure to this pesticide is the cause. Unable to work, he does not qualify for workers compensation because no doctor has yet implicated the linkage between his chemical exposure and seizures, a linkage necessary for a successful claim.

Yet carbaryl-related illnesses do occur in Washington. Between 1995 and 1999, the Department of Health documented eighteen incidents involving twenty-nine persons with acute symptoms following carbaryl exposure. Nine of those incidents occurred when the person mixing or applying carbaryl received a "splash" or came into direct contact with the spray.

These people suffered from various symptoms: nausea, headache, blurred vision, excess salivation, weakness, dizziness, eye irritation, skin irritation, and throat irritation. Eight incidents, involving eighteen people, occurred when carbaryl spray drifted over agriculture workers and neighbors. At the time of the Shoalwaters' dilemma, epidemiological studies were pointing to statistically significant associations between regular use of carbaryl by upland farmers and increased risk of non-Hodgkin's lymphoma, a cancer that starts in the lymph nodes.

The spraying on Willapa Bay continued un-interrupted even as the Shoalwater suffered infant mortalities, defects, miscarriages, molar pregnancies, and stillbirths. Tribal Chairman Herb Whitish wouldn't give up. "If they can't tell us what it is, we're looking for someone to tell us what it's not," he said. "I'd like to hear that our water is safe, that our land is safe, so we can have some comfort to stay where we are at."

Herb used the term "bureaucratic genocide" when referring to the pesticide use on cranberry bogs, forests, and oyster farms encircling the small tribe's reservation. Their troubles with stillbirths, miscarriages, and infant mortality skyrocketed; the tribe was in crisis. He argued that the Shoalwaters were the proverbial canary in the mine for the entire Willapa Bay.

"Everybody around here eats a lot of shellfish," Herb said. "But nobody is willing to make that leap from ingesting shellfish to an adverse outcome." Herb was not saying the shellfish were the cause, just one of many factors that should be investigated. However, the fear that environmental toxins might be responsible for the health crisis was widespread. "It's going to take a cooperative look by everyone in this area to find out what is going on. Putting chemicals into this environment is not good for any of us."

In 2000, Shoalwater Kim Zillyett was pregnant again after two miscarriages. In a *Seattle Post-Intelligencer* interview, she said that many women felt shame after miscarrying, and were traumatized by the plague of miscarriages. She said she "didn't eat or drink anything" near the reservation the first months of her pregnancy. At the time of her two miscarriages, she had lived a healthy lifestyle. "I take care of myself—no drinking, no drugs."

Concern about a potential connection with the widespread pesticide use wasn't limited to the birth crisis. Susan Crawford O'Brien included in her book, *Coming Full Circle,* Shoalwater Midge Porter's writing as part of a woman's writing group where she questioned other health linkages.

The cause of the deaths was never discovered.

For many of the Shoalwater, the loss of access to traditional foods—salmon and shellfish—was seen as another blow to their physiological and cultural existence. As one tribal woman explained, the pregnancy loss crisis was part of this long history of violence and loss, beginning with the epidemics and continuing with the loss of fishing rights. "So much has already been taken from the Shoalwater people, fishing rights, even the right to exist. Now babies are being taken." After a long history of inadequate healthcare, some felt that the state of Washington valued white-owned agricultural businesses more than the wellbeing of the Shoalwater people.

Ecology staff foreshadowed this sentiment. In an intense internal email exchange, Steve Saunders wrote to Mike Morhous, "EPA raised some very strong concerns regarding the use of chemicals to control burrowing shrimp (and spartina) in the recent report on the Shoalwater tribe's health problems. By ignoring these concerns, we are sending the message that the profit margin for the oyster industry is more important than the health of the tribal members."

Years later, meteorologist Cliff Mass echoed this same observation, when he blogged about yet another future proposed shellfish industry pesticide:

> Are you getting the idea that the Washington State Department of Ecology is more interested in protecting the bottom line of the oyster industry than protecting the health of Washington citizens and our natural environment? You would not be alone.

> And the bottom line of the oyster folks is doing very well, thank you. Here are some interesting statistics from the Washington State Department of Fish and Wildlife of the number of pounds of unshelled oysters produced in Washington each year and the price per pound. The harvest was level and the price QUADRUPLED (the reason is mainly because of loss of production in other parts of the world). Someone is making a LOT of money.

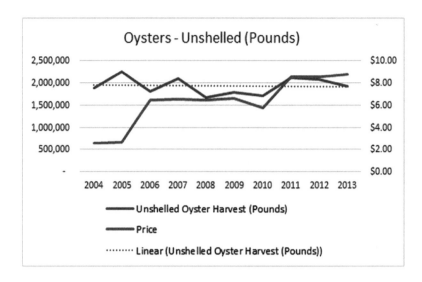

Oysters - Unshelled (Pounds)

In 1999, Ecology staff recommended three studies in light of the Shoalwater Bay Tribes crisis and evidence of carbaryl's persistence in Willapa Bay.

One of the recommended studies was to analyze carbaryl and its primary hydrolysis product, 1-napthol, in shellfish. Recommended sampling was to include tribal, public, and private sites. Ecology staff said this study was relatively easy to accomplish and less expensive than the other two studies: sediment and water quality testing.

Ecology did not conduct this recommended shellfish study. And, Ecology did not monitor or enforce the one-year harvest ban on sprayed oysters—oysters shipped all over the globe.

Carbaryl spraying continued throughout the 1990s in the war on shrimp, and glyphosate and imazapyr were added to the tank mix and put into the bay as part of the new war on spartina.

CHAPTER 10: ORGANIC GROWER?

L arry Warnberg had been growing oysters as organically as he could, given all the pesticides applied relentlessly near his tidelands, sometimes with the shrimp dying on his plot after the spray. In other words, not very organic. Sometimes shrimp would mysteriously die for several days in a row, even when there was no pesticide-spewing helicopter in sight.

Of course, he didn't advertise or market his oysters as organically grown; they couldn't be labeled organic, and he couldn't charge more for his oysters, so he lost a month's worth of harvest during the busiest time of the season. With the toxic carbaryl flying in the air, hitting the tideflats, becoming part of the water, and settling into sediments, how could Larry in good conscience harvest in July or August, when the annual spraying took place? He couldn't. And he didn't. But others did.

"They sprayed and harvested oysters, crabs, and clams throughout Willapa Bay. The state-issued pollution permit only prohibited harvest of oysters within one year on a directly sprayed plot ... with no routine monitoring. Harvest next door? No problem. Did any harvesting occur within that one-year prohibition period on the directly sprayed plot? Ecology chose not to monitor the oyster growers for compliance," Larry said. (Not only did Ecology NOT monitor the one-year harvest ban,

Ecology says they did not routinely test oysters, clams, or crabs after carbaryl spraying; nor did any other government agency.)

Larry, and Fritzi and Edward Cohen pleaded with Ecology to test for carbaryl in the sediments, the water, and the oysters, especially in light of the lack of rigorous agency monitoring as part of the state permits, and in light of all the occurrences of illegal spraying. "Contemporary accounts of illegal spraying and permit violations, such as spraying in 20-mile-per-hour winds and rain, make setting basic conditions both common sense and prudent where the oysters are being sold immediately to the public through hotels, restaurants, stores, U-pick, and to passersby and visitors to Long Beach Peninsula who are looking for good seafood and good oysters," the Cohens and Larry Warnberg wrote in a letter to Ecology in 1997.

Did shellfish patrons eating Willapa Bay or Grays Harbor oysters at oyster bars know they were consuming shellfish harvested "next door" from carbaryl-sprayed tidelands? "Next door" could be one foot, hundreds of feet, or a thousand feet away, where ample evidence said carbaryl concentrations were still toxic, just technically "off-site." Clams and crab from the contaminated water could be harvested too, and they were, if they were still alive.

Not only that, Ecology learned as early as 1998 that even at other times of the year, background levels of carbaryl in the water of Willapa Bay were documented to be above the recommended level that was safe for marine life.

Was this contamination harming marine life? Was it changing the ecosystem by selectively disadvantaging the more sensitive species?

Here's the rub. There was a one-year harvest ban on directly sprayed sites, but oysters exposed to the same levels of toxicity were okay to eat? Larry wasn't buying it. He was not aware of anyone else voluntarily suspending harvest in Willapa Bay except Edward and Fritzi Cohen, his neighbors to the south, who owned a boutique hotel. The Cohen's served his oysters as well as their own harvested from their tidelands to their hotel guests.

"It's a good occupation here. You're furnishing a good clean product."
Quote in *Willapa Bay Oysters* documentary.

Family shellfishing unaware of helicopter spraying behind them.
(Source: *The Oregonian*)

As early as 1961, and subsequently confirmed by study after study, the state agencies had unequivocal evidence that carbaryl drifted far offsite, and was just as toxic offsite as it was onsite. Larry allowed a month for the chemical pesticide to have time to dilute off his property, or photo-degrade into other stuff that might be a little less dangerous. But no state agency ever monitored his site, or any other sites, to ensure that the chemicals did not contaminate his oysters, although Larry repeatedly asked them to do so.

Ecology never monitored the one-year harvest prohibition although they knew that oyster tissue from treated beds had shown high carbaryl concentrations, in the tens of parts per million (ppm).

The EPA set a maximum concentration of carbaryl in oysters at .25 ppm, but Ecology said food purity wasn't its job; just water quality and sediment concentrations.

> Then, when Larry's neighbor sprayed four hundred feet from his site, Larry had dead fish and oysters from his tidelands sampled and they tested positive for carbaryl: .36 ppm of carbaryl in the oysters. Therein lays the dilemma: since Larry hadn't sprayed his oysters directly, he could have harvested them even though they were contaminated with carbaryl.

Larry found it difficult to get information from agency staff. They seemed to treat Larry as an enemy, even though internally some folks were pushing to do the same thing: stop the carbaryl spraying.

Ecology's Mark Bentley wrote in 1998, "…carbaryl should be phased out because it is bad for the environment, not driven by science, and a crutch for the industry." He also wondered, "…why should Ecology act as the growers' consultants for a product that poses unknown and likely significant environmental impacts, and why should we work towards development of an IPM when there is nothing indicating that an IPM will be successful?"

Nozzleheads

Larry watched as the shellfish companies violated the conditions of the state permit, particularly in compliance with the upper limit of 10 mph winds during spraying. "We observed aerial spraying in fifteen to twenty mph winds," he reported. Back in 1993, Ernie Summers, the Washington Dungeness Crab Association President, also witnessed such a violation and reported it at Senator Sid Snyder's large public meeting. Ernie had driven out to observe spraying near Elk River on Grays Harbor during high wind events, and reported that he could smell the carbaryl from where he was parked and that the wind gusts were greater than ten mph. But that was not the purpose of Senator Snyder's meeting.

Although Ernie had a lifetime of experience monitoring wind conditions out on the coast and in the bays, his concerns were dismissed. Senator Snyder directed the conversation away from Ernie to an oyster farmer and sprayer, "What I would like to get in a discussion of ... is the amount of acres being sprayed adequate?"

Larry observed other permit condition violations as well. "We witnessed spraying more than an hour after the low tide, whereas the permit stipulated no spraying thirty minutes after low tide. The permit required a two-hundred-foot spray buffer from channels and streams, and this was routinely ignored. Regarding the permit prohibition of not spraying oysters within one year of harvest, well, we observed spraying of mature marketable oysters."

The state required a 200-foot spray buffer from channels such as this in 1989.
(Source: Ecology)

"What monitoring there was showed repeated instances of drift offsite. No citations or enforcement actions were done by DOE. Asleep at the wheel? Or instructed by superiors to live and let live? Christine Gregoire was Ecology Director, then the Attorney General, then Governor during much of our struggles. She never helped us," Larry said.

"Hi, Janet," Larry wrote in 2000 to Ecology, "...I want to let you know that we've observed some dead shrimp in the oyster beds. This is highly unusual, raising suspicion about illegal spraying. We know there has been illegal carbaryl use in the past. Two years ago, WSU scientist Alan Schreiber was hired to test two other pesticides for local growers, but the test was unsuccessful because illegal carbaryl use contaminated the control plots[4]. It seems unlikely that you will catch growers using carbaryl without a permit, but you should know about this possibility and hopefully do some monitoring that might at least discourage the practice."

Ecology rejected Larry's suggestion to monitor as a deterrent. "There may be illegal spraying by those who do not go through the legal process of obtaining permits, but they are extremely difficult to document," Ecology's Mark Bentley responded to Larry's complaint. "Finally, carbaryl permits are one small fraction of Janet's responsibilities, and the permit is not fee-based. ... Certainly, we are not deputizing you to be an Ecology inspector, but a violation needs more documentation." Bentley highlighted one aspect of a no-fee permit: little to no oversight.

Ever hopeful, and taking Mark Bentley's enforcement needs to heart, Larry followed up with more detail: "Hi, Mark, there is new evidence to report concerning illegal carbaryl application in the

---

[4] The same thing was reported in the 1985 environmental analysis—carbaryl was detected in water samples PRIOR to spraying. The authors attributed this to contaminated samples, implying that there was a procedural error.

Nahcotta area. As the tide flooded in this morning, my helper and I spotted dozens of dead sculpin floating on the surface. This is highly unusual. If you read the Feldman report in the April 2000 issue of *Estuaries*, you may know that sculpin are a major predator of burrowing shrimp. When they eat poisoned shrimp, they also might die. Further evidence came just moments ago from a report by a shellfish farmer who attended a meeting this morning, convened by Wiegardt & Sons, and held at Jolly Roger Cannery here in Nahcotta where other companies stated that carbaryl was applied this morning to certain beds. Since DOE (Ecology) assumed major responsibility for managing the use of carbaryl, I hope you will investigate and take enforcement action."

Two retired fishermen, both involuntarily exposed to carbaryl, said in interviews for this book that they witnessed year-round carbaryl use. At one point, one of them even worked for a shellfish company. "We kept a coffee can of carbaryl in the boat. We would sprinkle it on the bed by hand," he said.

The other didn't work for a shellfish company, but he was frequently out on the water. "They would walk around the edges of their oyster beds sprinkling carbaryl to try to keep the shrimp out," he said, and then added, "I saw it all the time. Low tide, spring, or summer. Even if they don't get their annual permit, I think they will continue to use carbaryl. They need to keep using it to boost production."

"If you can't monitor effectively and stop chemical trespass, don't approve the permit," Larry suggested to Ecology's Mark Bentley in 2000.

Even though Larry Warnberg had a successful non-pesticide-dependent oyster operation, he was never interviewed by the state agencies during the preparation of the 1992 environmental analysis. He wasn't interviewed for the 1990-1991 Integrated Pest Management Plan (IPMP) prepared by the industry-heavy Burrowing Shrimp

Committee, the draft that state agencies wouldn't accept. Yet one of the reasons the IPMP was NOT acceptable to Fisheries and Ecology was because it did not include meaningful exploration of alternative growing methods—just like Larry's.

"All the while that the Shellfish Association members were spraying carbaryl nonstop with constant political pressure to spray for more shrimp habitat throughout the bays, I was making a living off of a sustainable farming technique. My farm was completely non-chemical dependent," Larry said. "In addition to not putting toxins into Willapa Bay, I developed positive relationships in the community with people who understood what the chemicals were doing to humans and to the environment. I sold oysters to several restaurants that wanted to serve toxin-free food."

Larry was just as pessimistic as Ernie Summers when the Burrowing Shrimp Committee was formed and tasked with developing an IPMP. He followed Fisheries' attempts to get the Shellfish Association to develop a true IPMP that was supposed to achieve a reduction in chemical reliance. But the status quo kept surfacing as the preferred alternative. Larry recalled, "As the '90s passed, the Growers did nothing to develop an IPMP, stalling as long as possible. I endearingly call them Nozzleheads."

In March 1992, an IPMP was issued by the Burrowing Shrimp Committee, but its credibility was smudged. Fisheries and Ecology shelved the document.

CONSOLIDATED POLITICAL CONTROL

The welfare of the state's waters and sediments depends on Ecology. Now that they had consolidated power as both the guardian of water and sediment quality, and were the state's sole pollution permit issuer, they became the target of intense political pressure by the oyster industry and politicians, led by Senator Sid Snyder. The Senator leaned on Ecology for the oyster industry, explaining that they needed the department to cooperate on a program to control shrimp. In Ecology's response back to Snyder, the native shrimp were "…these invasive pests." The Governor-appointed Ecology Director, Mary Riveland, promised that this was a high priority for the agency. Thus, Mary Riveland offered the agency's staff resources for facilitating permits, technical and financial assistance, and even legislative support, yet according to Ecology's own staff, they could not adequately monitor the spraying or to check on reports of illegal carbaryl use.

But before Ecology would allow an expansion in the sprayed acreage, they wanted the Burrowing Shrimp Committee to reconvene and develop an IPMP that explored non-chemical options, plus an implementation schedule. As part of the IPMP, the three agencies wanted an economic injury threshold documenting economic losses to the shellfish companies due to the native shrimp. But unlike Agriculture, both Fisheries and Ecology wanted to financially quantify impacts to other species, especially if they were going to increase the acres sprayed.

Revealing its narrow focus on profits, Agriculture wanted only documentation of economic injury to oyster growers, not losses to the environment.

Not wanting to re-live the debacle of the prior Burrowing Shrimp Committee, the three state agencies made some personnel changes on the committee, and hired a professional consultant to prepare the IPMP. Ecology led the effort and in 1995, awarded a $60,000 contract to Battelle's Sequim Marine Sciences Laboratory (Battelle), to be paid for with a combination of public funds and Shellfish Association money. The members of the Battelle research team included a shellfish company owner (and active carbaryl sprayer), and Dave Armstrong, appointed Director of the UW School of Fisheries (in 1999), whose 1990 study for the Shellfish Association[5] had concluded that killing crabs was good for crabs.[6]

But something happened along the way. The draft document was entitled, "Development of an Integrated Pest Management Plan..." In 1997, Battelle issued its final report, which became instead the "Evaluation of the Feasibility of Using Integrated Pest Management..." Its recommendations: business as usual and funding for more studies.

Two years and $60,000 later, the product had become a "framework for future research." Not only did the Battelle team not provide a pathway to either phase out the use of carbaryl, or greatly reduce the shellfish company's reliance on it, the Battelle team recommended that the state agencies make the *process to use carbaryl easier for the oyster farmers.* It also recommended public funding for the development and implementation of an IPMP. The document was characterized by Ecology staff as "the ... unsuccessful attempt to develop an IPM plan." They concluded that the document, like the original one prepared in the early 1990s, did not have sufficient detail envisioned by the state when it approved continued use of carbaryl in 1992 with the condition that an IPM be prepared.

Ecology staff extended an opportunity to review the document to the Oregon Department of Fish and Wildlife. Kim Jones responded: "The study does not adequately support the finding that use of carbaryl is the best (or even adequate) approach to controlling

---

[5] The study also lists the state, Pacific County, and UW's Sea Grant Program as sponsors.

[6] In 1996, after the Battelle project was underway, Ecology Deputy Director Terry Husseman wrote in reference to issues with the IPMP project, "As I recall, part of the problem was due to the lack of cooperation by the oyster growers. Since they are not hesitant about calling us to task for our unwillingness to do precisely what they want us to do exactly when they want us to do it, have you been able to convince them of the importance of their cooperation in this project?"

ghost and mud shrimp." Jones concluded, "Overall, I think a tremendous amount of detail was presented on burrowing shrimp biology and on how an IPMP works, but very little scientific information to support the use of carbaryl to control burrowing shrimp. The conclusions are not supported by the document."

To put a finer point on the lack of scientific information to support the use of carbaryl to control burrowing shrimp, EPA's Mike Marsh pointed out in his review of the program, "Since chemicals have been used in Willapa Bay since the early 1960s, one wonders how effective they have been, or whether they have actually been a contributing factor in the increase of burrowing shrimp densities (perhaps by eliminating a competitor or predator)." Indeed, carbaryl was fatal and/or toxic to many aquatic animals that were predators of the shrimp: crab, sturgeon, sculpin, salmon, sole, cutthroat trout, herring. All this was known, yet the shellfish companies persisted in disrupting the entire balance in these bays, for their profit.

The green sturgeon was a major shrimp predator, but its populations are now so low that it has been listed under the ESA. Is it possible that the annual spraying of carbaryl contributed to its decline?

According to NMFS, fish exposed to carbaryl through direct uptake from the water column and across the gills, ingestion of carbaryl in the sediment, and in their food, has an adverse impact. Not only did the carbaryl kill the sturgeon's main prey, is it possible that the sharp oyster shells that they place on the former shrimp habitat harmed the sturgeon? Sturgeon use their mouth like a vacuum hose to suck up benthic prey. Since oyster ground culture converts soft bottom habitat to more of a "rocky" (shell-covered) substrate, some are concerned that the oysters could impede feeding, forcing sturgeon to burn energy by having to search for critical food elsewhere.

Larry watched as the Committee droned on, allowing the spraying to continue, year after year. It was apparent to him that Ecology was not protecting the environment. But Ecology could point to the Burrowing Shrimp Committee as "A safe, bureaucratic way to gain a desired outcome." Meanwhile carbaryl spraying, and industry and publicly funded science machinery continued unabated. Ecology gradually adopted the position that the spray program had only short-term impacts and was therefore not a long-term program.

There was no integrated pest management plan progress, no reduction in pesticide use, no oversight. Nothing. Non-compliance was pervasive. Ecology allowed continued non-compliance with the hypothetical IPMP that was supposed to have reduced pesticide use. Ecology allowed continued non-compliance with the 1992 documents that had required the IPMP. And, going even deeper, Ecology allowed non-compliance with the state water quality administrative code that required an IPMP for any on-going long-term operation and maintenance program. Surely, after thirty plus years the annual spraying of the estuaries constituted an on-going long-term operation?

According to Steve Saunders, who worked for Ecology during this era and is now retired, "This was a high-profile political issue from the governor's office, the legislature, to individual state agencies. Ground culture of oysters and dredging is a high-profit operation for many of the oyster growers. They don't want to do the long-line or stake operation like Larry used because it's less profitable. Since they are driven by their own economic advantage, they want to continue the high profit ground culture and dredge culture of oysters. Anything that interferes with this is unacceptable to them."

Instead, hundreds of thousands of public dollars, funneled through state agencies, were spent on study after study, including studies of replacement pesticides—to protect and expand the oyster industry. The primary state agencies that subsidized pesticides in Willapa Bay included Fish and Wildlife (formerly Department of Fisheries until 1994), Ecology, Agriculture, and the Washington Commission on Pesticide Registration. Each agency spends public funds on these programs while assuring the public that this is a safe practice.

NATIONAL ORGANIC STANDARDS

On a parallel track to the Burrowing Shrimp Committee, Larry followed what he thought would be the development of National Organic Standards for aquaculture. He was hoping that either the IPMP or an organic standard—whichever came first—would serve as a catalyst to phase out the use of pesticides in the estuaries. The timing was fortuitous since the 1990s were pivotal to the development of national organic standards for upland agriculture. Larry thought he could help develop organic standards for aquaculture as part of the process for upland organic standards. His goal was to keep pesticides out of the water and off his oysters.

Forever hopeful, Larry soon realized that the IPMP and Organic Aquaculture Standards were going nowhere.

"Standards for aquaculture were contentious from the start, so the USDA National Organic Standards Board punted over the years," Larry recalled. "I wrote letters galore; perhaps others did too, hoping for standards that would give shellfish growers some protection from pesticide drift and chemical trespass. The Net-Pen Salmon Farming companies were the loudest opponents, and the oyster companies lobbied too."

The Organic Foods Production Act was passed by the U.S. Congress in 1990, and the United States Department of Agriculture (USDA) issued its first draft of standards in the National Organic Program in 1997 ... with no aquaculture standards.

Larry continued, "Around 2000, the National Organic Standards Board appointed an eleven-member Aquaculture Working Group to develop long overdue aquaculture standards. The director of the Pacific Coast Shellfish Growers Association got one of those eleven seats."

Founded in 1930, the Pacific Coast Shellfish Growers Association, with its tagline of "Partners with Mother Nature," was originally founded to find markets and stabilize prices. According to its website, the Association later broadened its scope to include anti-pollution activities, which they claim remains a critical mission (this industry association is larger than the Willapa/Grays Harbor Oyster Growers Association, and is based in Olympia.)

Larry sums up, "It's not surprising to me that to this day, there are still no organic aquaculture standards because pesticide use wouldn't be allowed, contaminant testing of the animals would be required, and the triploid oyster may not qualify for labeling as organic."

MUTANT OYSTER

The story of the triploid Pacific oyster is certainly big enough to warrant a book of its own. It was almost the first chromosomally modified organism to be granted a U.S. Patent, and the only reason that its inventor, Stanford Allen, was NOT granted his patent was because he published too many details before he filed his patent. Triploidy occurs in some cells in nature, but not in any of the cells in "natural" oysters. Most life forms that reproduce sexually are diploid; they have two sets of chromosomes. Triploidy involves creating an organism that has a third set of chromosomes because organisms with three sets of chromosomes are sterile, and as a result, they do not go through a messy, metabolically expensive, hormone-dominated reproductive phase. Which means that in contrast to "natural oysters," triploid oysters can be harvested at any time of year except during a "red tide," which happens when the water column is contaminated with dinoflagellates that produce paralytic shellfish toxins and make shellfish unsafe to eat. Harvesting oysters year-round means more money for the shellfish companies, so a chromosomally modified oyster that could increase profits was very much worth fighting for.

Although the Aquaculture Working Group, including the representative from the Pacific Coast Shellfish Growers Association, couldn't recommend the development of an organic standard for mollusks in 2001, they *could* recommend that a chromosomally modified oyster be allowed as organic.

However, the Organic Foods Production Act of 1990 prohibited aquatic animals designated as triploidy to be sold as organic. Possibly even more problematic for the Washington State shellfish companies was the prohibition of harvesting an animal off land within three years of applying chemicals.

To this day, aquatic foods are the only major food category not included in the national organic standards regulation. There are standards for organic vegetables, cereal, soup, beans, pasta, pasta sauce, bread, flour, chocolate, beef, chicken, egg, pork, lamb, pork, cotton, makeup, deodorants, shampoo, hair conditioner, soap, condoms, even honey, but no standard for oysters.

CHAPTER 11: GOTCHA!

Since the spraying of carbaryl started so soon after the end of World War II—followed by the global proliferation of chemicals including pesticides—there weren't many laws regulating its use, or government agencies to protect human health or the environment. Some say we still don't have such agencies.

Regulatory capture is a theory associated with George Stigler, a Nobel laureate economist. It is the process by which regulatory agencies eventually come to be dominated by the very industries they were charged with regulating. Regulatory capture happens when a regulatory agency, formed to act in the public's interest, eventually acts in ways that benefit the industry it is supposed to be regulating, rather than benefiting the public. Public interest agencies that come to be controlled by the industry they were charged with regulating are known as "captured agencies." Regulatory capture is gamekeeper turned poacher.

Entire state governments can fall victim to regulatory capture. These states then become the voice of the industry, even to the point of blocking national policies that would be preferred by the majority across the whole federation.

Regulatory capture occurs because groups, or individuals with a high-stakes interest in the outcome of policy or regulatory decisions, focus their resources and energies in attempting to gain the policy outcomes they prefer. Members of the public, each with only a tiny individual stake in the outcome, either ignore the issue, or don't have the resources to "capture" the agency or fight it. Larry's group obviously hadn't captured Ecology, since a captured agency will implement the preferred policy outcomes of the special interest group that controls it. So those that wanted pesticide-free shellfish had to fight Ecology.

APPEAL #1

"We exhausted all democratic avenues to have our concerns addressed and we were ignored. So we turned to the judicial system," Larry recalled. "We filed our first appeal of the annual state pollution permit in 2000, and were ignored."

The appeals were filed by the Ad Hoc Coalition for Willapa Bay, formed in 1989 by Larry, and Fritzi and Edward Cohen, with the primary purpose to keep chemicals out of the estuary. "By then, it was clear that the National Organic Standards Board wasn't going to adopt organic standards for shellfish, thanks to lobbying on behalf of the shellfish industry. This left us with only one option: formal appeals and lawsuits," Larry said.

In their efforts to gain public momentum for their first appeal, the Ad Hoc Coalition for Willapa Bay mounted an outreach campaign. Hundreds of people sent emails and comments to Ecology, pleading with them to stop spraying these estuaries with a neurotoxin.

Tobiah Israel wrote that there were 352 certified shellfish farms in the state, but "Only eighteen have applied for the spray permit, clearly a minority that is willing to risk public health and environmental integrity by persisting in the use of a potent non-selective pesticide." He went on to say, "A scientist from WSDOE discovered in 1998 that significant levels of carbaryl and its toxic breakdown products were found in many areas of Willapa Bay months after spraying occurred. The report was suppressed for a year, and then dismissed as unreliable." The report Israel referenced was known as the "Stonick Study," prepared by Ecology's Cynthia Stonick.

Scott Gatzke, who lived on Willapa Bay in Ocean Park, had substantive concerns including the way Ecology was dismissing hard evidence prepared by its own staff (the Stonick Study) documenting widespread toxicity of carbaryl and persistence in the water column and sediments, not previously reported by the Shellfish Association.

He wrote:

As you know, every state with an oystering industry, *other than Washington*, has banned the use of carbaryl in aquatic environments as unsafe and a risk to the health of the ecosystem and humans. Further, Ecology has information prepared by its own staff that supports this view.

Ecology's Stonick Study, dated May 1999, drew several profound conclusions:

1) Monitoring of the spraying is inadequate;
2) there is no plan to evaluate adverse long-term impacts on biological resources in Willapa Bay resulting from the use of carbaryl;
3) the presence of carbaryl on day-60 indicates carbaryl is persisting in the marine environment;
4) due to drift, a larger area is being treated with carbaryl than the allowable acreage;
5) carbaryl concentrations in pore-water of all three spray sites exceeded the National Academy of Sciences and Engineering water quality recommendations;
6) chronic toxicity experiments for 10 weeks in sediment with carbaryl in overlying water indicated that the average number of larval invertebrate non-target species ... were significantly reduced.

Gatzke said the Shellfish Association's argument that spraying carbaryl was good for species diversity was bogus and that Ecology should be able to see through that falsehood. He continued:

> There are some straightforward and obvious conclusions that can be drawn from the continued use of carbaryl in Willapa Bay. Ecology's own research concludes that the product inevitably drifts onto non-target areas; no research has been done on long-term exposure of carbaryl to invertebrates, salmon, crab, or birds that opportunistically feed off the dead ghost shrimp; unsafe concentrations of carbaryl persist in sediment; oystermen have misrepresented the value of carbaryl use as promoting specie diversification; there are indications of illegal spraying (per the Stonick Study and from sworn affidavits of independent oyster growers who saw concentrations of dead shrimp on their beds as recently as last week); and, most disturbing of all, *there is inadequate monitoring of carbaryl applications in Willapa Bay*. This is from Ecology's own research.

But Gatzke knew the score. "I am aware that Ecology is not funded in a way to properly monitor the spraying. I am also aware that the oystermen have the political will and access to push this application. However, one day soon, this program will inevitably end, and when it does we will all look back and say, 'Why didn't we do it sooner?'"

C. Payne wrote what must have been the shortest and sweetest comment letter ever written: *"Mr. Bentley, I have just one comment: DON'T."*

But Ecology did. The annual, business-as-usual state permit was issued, and the shellfish companies sprayed again in 2000.

HEADWATERS RULING

Finally, a significant event occurred on March 12, 2001, one that gradually changed the course of the carbaryl-spraying program. On that day, the Ninth Circuit Court of Appeals announced its decision on the *Headwaters, Inc. v. Talent Irrigation District* case (*Headwaters* ruling), changing the state regulatory structure for point-source application of pesticides into water bodies.

This case stipulated that a permit administered under the federal Clean Water Act, was needed to apply aquatic herbicides or algaecides, which were considered pollutants, directly to water bodies. This was not a state Short-Term Water Quality Modification Permit (state permit), but a federal permit issued under a federal program.

The Clean Water Act prohibits any point-source discharge of a pollutant into waters of the United States—unless the discharge is in compliance with certain sections of the Clean Water Act. One way a person may discharge pollutants without violating this prohibition is by obtaining authorization from the EPA under another federal permit—a NPDES permit. Since 1973, the EPA had delegated responsibility of administration of this program to various states, including Washington's Department of Ecology.

The state that had permitted carbaryl since 1963, could no longer deny the requirement for a federal permit. There was one catch: Ecology also administered these federal permits.

When this precedent-setting case law came down in March 2001, it occurred inconveniently, just around the corner from the annual spray regimen. Like clockwork for thirty-eight years, carbaryl spraying was ramped up every June and was completed by August, year after year after year. What was Ecology to do? There was not enough time to comply with the circuit court ruling, and go through the federal permit process before the 2001 spray season ... so Ecology issued the state permit. Compliance with the new federal law didn't fit with the annual spray schedule.

Scott Gatzke again wrote to Ecology. "There is no language in the *Headwaters* ruling that gives the permitting authority discretion as to when the ruling is to be applied. It serves no legitimate purpose to ignore the clear language of *Headwaters* and proceed as if it doesn't exist."

However, heartfelt and articulate citizen complaints could be ignored by the evidently now-captured Ecology, and that's what Ecology did. Ecology issued the annual state pollution permit in 2001, in the face of new case law mandating a federal permit, and re-adopted the outdated 1992 environmental analysis that Ecology openly admitted was incomplete.

Out of fear of a lawsuit over Ecology's issuance of the wrong pollution permit, the carbaryl applicants opted to not spray in 2001, even though they had state approval. For the first time in almost forty years, the shellfish companies did not spray carbaryl, but not because of the ten million animals killed and the widespread contamination of the Willapa Bay and Grays Harbor estuaries, but *out of fear of a lawsuit*.

The shellfish companies complained that not spraying in 2001 would result in the loss of $20 million, their estimated value of the 2004 and 2005 crops of oysters dependent on the 2001 spray season. As industry chroniclers said before, oysters are "Big Business."

APPEAL #2

The Ad Hoc Coalition for Willapa Bay appealed Ecology's 2001 state permit, arguing that inconvenience was not a strong enough basis to ignore the *Headwaters* ruling that now required compliance with the Clean Water Act and issuance of a federal permit. The appeal was not heard.

Gerald Swan, of Grass Creek Oyster Company, wrote to Ecology about the appeal, "These efforts are selfishly misguided and will result in a major degradation of the marine environment and the continued downward spiral of endangered marine species." Swan argued, contrary to the *Headwaters* ruling, that carbaryl was not a pollutant, but was an essential part of the marine environment. "Burrowing shrimp populations have to be controlled to promote healthy marine environments, and until nature is able to take over that control, we need to help nature along with beneficial pesticide applications. Further, it should be recognized that, since applications of this product enhance and promote the survival of marine endangered species, the pesticide product is more of adjunct to the marine environment rather than a pollutant, and as such, may not require an NPDES permit."

STATE ISSUES MULTI-YEAR FEDERAL POLLUTION PERMIT

Taylor Shellfish wrote a letter to Ecology and pressed them to issue the court-ordered federal permit "...no later than the end of June 2002." This would allow the shellfish companies to make the annual sprayings that usually occurred in July and August.

On one hand, Taylor Shellfish assured Ecology that "...we as an industry are very committed to protecting the delicate marine ecosystem...."

On the other hand, Taylor Shellfish asked Ecology to expedite permit approval to spray carbaryl, a neurotoxin and nerve agent, into that same delicate marine ecosystem: "The purpose of this letter is to reemphasize how critical it is for our industry to have the NPDES permits in place to be able to spray carbaryl by July 2002." Taylor Shellfish explained why this was so important:

Chapter 11: Gotcha!

Control of burrowing shrimp in Willapa Bay and Grays Harbor is absolutely essential to the survival of the industry in those bays. The industry in these two bays produces roughly 60 percent of the oysters on the West Coast of the United States. Of the 10,000 acres farmed in Willapa and Grays, only 800 are permitted to be treated annually. This barely allows the industry to stay on top of the problem when beds on average need to be retreated ever (sic) 4 to 6 years. The 800 acres lost by not being able to spray this year for lack of permits will likely be lost forever. We can't make that up next year as there are other beds scheduled to be sprayed. This represents millions of dollars of lost revenue and crucial jobs in a rural economy that is already depressed. Another year without the ability to spray will likely spell the demise of a number of companies.

Taylor Shellfish assured Ecology that they were an important ally when it came to protecting water quality:

Not getting a permit will mean the end of a 150-year industry … that has a history of stewardship over those bays. This is an ally that I believe DOE (Ecology) will sorely miss when it comes to defending water quality and the new shoreline guidelines … We have always worked cooperatively with DOE. Our agendas to protect the environment are parallel.

On May 17, 2002, with continued reliance on the 1992 environmental documents that Ecology itself said were incomplete, and having to endure two public hearings where the public turned out to decry the use of carbaryl, and in receipt of many letters in opposition to the continued spraying of carbaryl, Ecology issued a four-year federal permit to the Shellfish Association.

Ecology granted the Shellfish Association new multi-year permit "on time," and was forced to substantially reduce the permit fee.

Larry Warnberg recalls, "When the *Headwaters* court decision ruled that pesticide discharges into water required an NPDES permit, Ecology went through the year-long process, held public hearings, wrote the permit, and estimated that it would cost $50,000." Larry paused and continued, "There is a state law requiring permittees to pay the full cost of developing and monitoring an NPDES permit. The Growers went to State Senator Sid Snyder, who promptly got a bill passed through both Houses and signed by Governor Christine Gregoire reducing the permit fee to $300 per year, passing along the cost to the public. I screamed and hollered over this fee reduction, but got no response. Doesn't seem fair to the taxpaying public."

The Controversy Just Won't Go Away

Ecology issued the permit in the face of mounting significant federal, state, and citizen concerns, as well as the Shoalwaters' continuing concerns that carbaryl could be linked to a high rate of miscarriages, birth defects, and other problems for the seafood subsistent tribe that lived on Willapa Bay.

NMFS, again, wrote a sizzling letter and strongly suggested that Ecology not issue the permit for the normal full five years given the "uncertainties" surrounding this program, plus the number of outstanding studies YET TO BE CONDUCTED.

Harkening back to the two environmental analyses from 1985 and 1992, NMFS found misleading information, questionable assertions, bias, omitted key facts, and misleading statements.

NMFS suggested that Ecology's Fact Sheet should at least acknowledge that after the poisoning of the shrimp, the shrimp were the first colonizer species to return to the "disturbed area." Indeed, two people interviewed for this book grew up on Willapa Bay and said they watched the cyclic poisoning of traditional shrimp grounds, which were then planted with Pacific oysters, and then poisoned again as the shrimp re-colonized their habitat once the level of poison subsided.

In responding to comments, Ecology did not provide a larger discussion about the toxicology of carbaryl, the natural function of burrowing shrimp, and the potential impacts to other resources as well as a more balanced presentation as to the environmental impacts of carbaryl. Ecology did not provide information regarding the number of acres historically inhabited by the shrimp prior to the removal of the native Olympia oyster, and subsequent intensive oyster farming in the estuaries.

In the permit, mixing zones are allowed under a concept called All Known, Available, and Reasonable Methods of Treatment (AKART) that even Ecology admits is hard for them to grasp. Ecology's Water Quality Program Permit Writer's Manual for its staff advises, "AKART has been interpreted as a technology-based approach to limiting pollutants from wastewater discharges that requires an engineering judgment and an economic judgment. Because AKART encompasses a complex process of engineering and economic decision-making **there can be no simple definition**."

There is no simple definition of what AKART means, but future Ecology documents indicate that AKART could be defined as an Integrated Pest Management Plan, which they still didn't have. The Shellfish Association did not have such a plan; evidently, their plan was just to keep using pesticides as long as the state would allow it.

NMFS asked Ecology how they could grant a mixing zone without AKART, because mixing zones were allowed only under AKART. In the draft permit, Ecology included a "mixing zone" of 600 meters offset from each spray site. So NMFS asked, how big is the mixing zone? Since the mixing zone would depend on the size, location, and shape of the treated parcel, NMFS estimated that the impacted area along a shoreline parcel could be twice as large as the area "treated." And an area sprayed in the middle of the bay would have an even larger mixing zone, where acute and chronic toxicity was going to be allowed.

How big is this area? Ecology did not answer the question. But in other responses, they stuck to their party line: "The limited area treated each year (600 acres in Willapa Bay and 200 acres in Grays Harbor) is considered acceptable at present."

Not only did NMFS press Ecology for a true accounting of the pollution in acres—obviously way more than the 800 acres directly sprayed, NMFS asked how Ecology could grant the Shellfish Association the right to pollute other private and public tidelands? Others asked the same question. This would amount to an endorsement of chemical trespass and raise all kinds of property rights and environmental damage issues. So Ecology deleted the 600-meter offset and the proposed mixing zone, and authorized chemical trespass disappeared from Ecology permit documents:

> Ecology's Response to Comment 34: "The 600-meter offset in
> the permit has been *deleted (emphasis added)*. The water
> quality modification applies only to waters of the state, and
> does not authorize chemical trespass."

Ecology made the mixing zones and chemical trespass go away … *on paper*. But Ecology knew that carbaryl drifted within the estuaries, with mortal toxicities offsite equivalent to a directly sprayed site. Ecology also knew that background levels of carbaryl had been found to be above safe levels for marine life.

NMFS probed deeper. What was the toxicity of carbaryl when the poison from two sprayed sites spread and then combined in these mixing zones? Wouldn't the levels be in higher concentrations, since the actual carbaryl didn't just magically disappear like the mixing zones did from Ecology's permit? So what were those compounded levels? For example, if two sprayed sites were separated by 50 feet, and carbaryl came from each site at the intended concentrations that would kill almost all invertebrates on a target site, and these meet in that overlap, what would that toxicity concentration be? How long would it endure? And who would account for this? Would it be monitored?

Ecology's response? "The current permit does not include mixing zones." Not only did Ecology dodge the issue of chemical trespass by deleting mixing zones, they accepted the Shellfish Association's non-compliance with the required IPMP, and non-compliant annual spraying, as ... *compliant.*

Whoopsie Daisy

In what appeared to be open warfare within DFW—two dramatically different comment letters were submitted to Ecology.

One letter, not by any stretch a favorable letter, was submitted on behalf of an entire agency program. The other was submitted by an individual who wrote that he was the agency representative who deals directly with this issue and argued for continued use of chemicals.

The first letter was submitted by the Habitat Program on April 9, 2002. This program suggested that the EPA be brought in to review the Ecology permit, citing complexities and concern regarding the continued carbaryl spraying.

The second letter supported continued use of chemicals: "While it would be desirable to find substitutes for chemical application, true IPM does not preclude chemical use, and we may find that chemicals need to be used in concert with these alternative measures." That second letter, submitted by a single DFW employee, stated that the preferred alternative was to kill the native shrimp and replace them with non-native oysters, and that spraying was a short-term necessity to achieve this longer-term goal of habitat modification. He referred to carbaryl as a "vector" to transmit fatal doses to the native shrimp: "The chemical is really a vector and has relatively short-term effects even if it persists at very low levels for 140 days in some areas as your data suggests."

In 1999, he cautioned Stonick in her use of the term "ecosystem disruption" where she wrote:

> Thirty-six years ago, when carbaryl was first used in the marine environment, agencies did not understand environmental toxicity, much less carcinogenicity and mutagenicity. EPA has recently placed carbaryl on its list of endocrine disrupters for fin fish and avian reproduction (EPA 1997). Washington State has serious concerns about anthropogenic disturbances that have potential to affect the fate of salmon. At this time, while we endeavor to save salmon, carbaryl should come under the same scrutiny as any other substance that causes ecosystem disruption.

What is ecosystem disruption if not the removal of a keystone native species by using a toxic chemical in an effort to benefit a non-native species, along with the collateral killing of over 10 million fish, crab, worms, and shrimp? All this, plus unstudied impacts up the food chain—in estuaries with species on the brink of extinction.

This DFW staff person concluded, "Burrowing shrimp are removed. They profoundly influence the type of organisms present and therefore the food web, competition, and predator prey relationships due to constant bioturbation of the sediments. They are replaced with a stable substrate and oysters, a three-dimensional structural habitat that has similar far-reaching effects. This point continues to be ignored by just about everyone concerned with the use of pesticides. It shouldn't diminish that concern, but habitat change needs to at least be acknowledged as the primary effect observed in the field!"

"He was initially concerned with the carbaryl spraying program," recalled retired Ecology employee Steve Saunders in an interview for this book. "But eventually that DFW staff person became an industry supporter."

CUBICLE COURAGE

Fortunately, others working within state and federal agencies were deeply disturbed with the spray program. They turned to the Public Employees for Environmental Responsibility (PEER), a national organization of public employees formed just for this purpose— public employees standing up for the environment.

PEER is a national non-profit alliance of local, state, and federal scientists, law enforcement officers, land managers, and other professionals dedicated to upholding environmental laws and values. According to PEER, "We have the distinct honor of serving resource professionals who daily cast profiles in courage in cubicles across the country."

Lea Mitchell's comments, as the Washington Director of PEER, appealed to Ecology to get down to the truth of the matter and back to core values. To get real. Mitchell called Ecology out on the carpet. "We find that the draft permit coupled with the government's failure to help finance alternatives to pesticide use, will likely perpetuate a shell game that has been going on for two decades with limited progress towards a viable alternative to spraying pesticides on tidelands."

Mitchell told Ecology "...to put on waders and venture into unknown territory and mandate a phase out carbaryl." She asserted, "Ecology should refrain from issuing a permit that in essence attempts to make legal an illegal practice that for over two decades the industry has been asked—but never mandated—to phase out."

To sanction the myth that spraying carbaryl into the estuarine ecosystems was harmless required a menu of tactics: unsubstantiated claims; omitted unfavorable facts; high, or no, mortality thresholds; delayed toxicity testing to allow for dilution; no testing of birds; no testing of shellfish; no agency monitoring; overlooked violation complaints, and no plan to stop pesticide use.

Mitchell summed up, "Overall we find the draft permit to violate the goals and policies of state and federal laws regarding water quality, sediments, and the protection of aquatic life."

That's all. What more did Ecology need?

To perpetuate this program, Ecology had to ignore what was happening to endangered species. Mitchell called them out on this too, "We also find that the permit relies, in part, on an incomplete Supplemental Environmental Impact Statement completed ten years ago when environmental conditions and the status of fisheries stocks was significantly different. Cutthroat spawning habitat occurs in the tributaries of Willapa Bay and Grays Harbor, sturgeon migrate to the estuaries from the lower Columbia, and five species of salmon are present in Willapa Bay. Sturgeon are in decline, Coho in Willapa Bay are candidates for Endangered Species Act listing, and listing of cutthroat trout has been proposed. The agencies have a mandatory responsibility to protect the public interest in viable populations of these fish." But who was Ecology protecting? The animals? The environment? The public? Or the shellfish industry?

This is what Ecology decided:
Carbaryl applied in Willapa Bay and Grays Harbor is toxic to shrimp, crabs, small fish, and certain worms. The limited area treated each year (600 acres in Willapa Bay and 200 acres in Grays Harbor) is considered acceptable at present.

Ecology issued the multi-year federal permit.

PESTICIDE ADVISORY

OYSTER TIDELANDS IN
THIS AREA WILL BE
TREATED WITH THE
INSECTICIDE "SEVIN"
FOR FURTHER
INFORMATION CALL:
(360) 665-XXXX FRITZ WIEGARDT
(360) 665-XXXX DENNIS TUFTS
(360) 665-XXXX MIKE LYNN

WARNING

(Source: Ecology)

Chapter 12: Third Time's A Charm

L
arry Warnberg and Fritzi Cohen, as the Ad Hoc Coalition for Willapa Bay, filed their third and final appeal of the carbaryl program, in 2002. But things were different this time; they weren't alone. The Washington Toxics Coalition, which works to protect public health and the environment by eliminating toxic pollution, joined with them and brought resources, but perhaps more importantly, the Washington Toxics Coalition was based in Seattle — the largest city in the state, and located on Puget Sound.

Oyster Mecca

In Seattle, Willapa Bay is renowned for its oysters, but not for the historical and ongoing use of pesticides, and the shellfish companies weren't advertising their annual injection of 6,400 pounds of carbaryl, imazamox, or the imidacloprid now pending in the wings. Seattle people dining on oysters don't know about the chronic pesticide use.

There are 3,358 restaurants in Seattle, and 141 of those are seafood restaurants. Coupled with the intensive marketing of oysters as a healthy lifestyle choice, restaurants market themselves as "oyster bars." Taylor Shellfish, at one time one of the leading pesticide advocates[7], is breaking into the Seattle market with their own "branded" oyster bars.

Seattle is marketed as the most creative oyster region in the world, where nowhere else can you taste so many different flavors and styles of oysters—with the classic flavor profile described as "sweet and funky." Seattle is touted as "the most intense oyster town in the country."

Diners in Seattle can ask for Willapa Bay oysters when ordering, and are encouraged to experience eating an oyster just like drinking a fine wine. Oysters are marketed as having a unique *merroir*, the marine counterpart of *terroir*, displaying all those environmental aspects that shape the taste of wine. For oysters, *merroir* is the flavor-defining characteristics that come from the waters where the oysters matured: the varieties of plankton the oysters ate, the type of water filtering through it, all of the elements of its environment are present in the oyster's flavor—just as a wine reveals elements of its upbringing at first sip.

Author Rowan Jacobson guides consumers through a gastronomique six-part oyster-tasting journey:

1) The bouquet. Just as you do with a glass of wine, begin by inhaling the aroma of the oyster;
2) The liqueur. Sipping the "juice" in which the oyster sits can tell you a lot about where it's from. That's where you get the first hits of salinity, minerality, earthiness;
3) The front. With the oyster in your mouth, focus on the taste

---

[7] According to a statement prepared for the 2002 Willapa Coalitions Pollution Control Hearings Board appeal, Bill Dewey declared he started work for Taylor Shellfish in 1991 dealing with permits, regulatory affairs and marketing. "For approximately the past six years Taylor has been farming in Willapa Bay and I have become involved in the carbaryl spray program. During that time I have taken a leadership role for the industry on the issue...."

with the tip of your tongue. This introduces you to the initial flavor, which may then change as you eat it;

4) The body. As you chew the actual oyster itself, concentrate on the texture as well as the flavor;

5) The finish. Oysters linger on the palate longer than a lot of foods. The finish is often when you taste the oyster's umami, that undercurrent of savory flavor;

6) The pairing. An oyster matched with the right wine or beer is like a perfect marriage.

The pesticides' toxic mist spewing from a low flying helicopter onto tideflats in front of million dollar homes around Seattle or Hood Canal would create an entirely different *merroir*.

But Willapa Bay and Grays Harbor oysters aren't just served in Seattle. Washington State, one of the largest producers of hatchery-reared and farmed shellfish in the U.S., produces 25 to 33 percent of the nation's oysters, and Willapa Bay and Grays Harbor account for over 60 percent of the state's production, and the largest shellfish company in the United States used pesticides. The company that owns the largest oyster-shucking facility on the West Coast did too. They used carbaryl, imidacloprid, are permitted to use, and have used imazamox, and one of these companies is featured in *Willapa Bay Oysters* boxing up and shipping oysters, including boxes addressed to a popular Seattle area seafood restaurant chain.

What if consumers, all over the globe, knew that the oysters, crabs, clams, and fish from these two coastal bays were annually exposed to pesticides?

On June 25, 2002, the Washington Toxics Coalition and the Ad Hoc Coalition for Willapa Bay, referred to as the Willapa Coalitions, filed an appeal of the Ecology-issued permit with the Washington State Pollution Control Hearings Board (Board).

Simultaneously, they requested a stay to stop the planned July and August spraying until the appeal was heard and decided. The Willapa Coalitions argued that the federal permit was little changed from the previous state permit, which, in effect, allowed the shellfish companies another spray season with no meaningful parameters. The battle was on.

The Board's three members are appointed by the Governor. Its purpose is to hear appeals of orders and decisions made by state agencies. Its sole function is to provide litigants a full and complete administrative hearing, as **promptly as possible**, followed by a **fair and impartial** written decision based on facts and law *(emphasis added)*.

In theory, the Board is not affiliated with Ecology or any other state agency, yet there is one powerful common thread — the Governor. The Governor appoints the Board, the Governor appoints the Director of Ecology, and both collect state salaries. The Board, ignoring its sole function up to this point, had refused to hear all prior Ad Hoc Coalition for Willapa Bay's appeals, one in 2000 and 2001.

But then, in 2002, the Board was evidently reluctant to ignore an appeal that the Seattle-based Washington Toxics Coalition had signed on to. Ecology joined with the Shellfish Association to fight the appeal and defend the permit that many considered illegal. Their first action was to fight the Willapa Coalitions' request to stop the 2002 spraying. The three-member Board voted 2 to 1 to grant the stay. This ruling did not last long.

The Board granted the stay and the Shellfish Association immediately appealed to the Thurston County Superior Court. The Shellfish Association argued that an overriding public interest to control native shrimp would be violated, and that native shrimp damaged the environment as well the shellfish industry. On July 19, 2002, Judge Paula Casey overturned the Board's decision, allowing the shellfish companies to spray on the following Monday, July 22.

MORE, MORE, MORE

Not only did Ecology fight the stay that could have prevented the 2002 spraying, they granted approval to spray an all-time high area encompassing 1,000 acres. And, the appeal had not yet been heard.

To bring an appeal or lawsuit regarding a permit, an appellant must have standing, which means that only those with enough direct stake in an action can challenge it. Larry Warnberg and Fritzi Cohen had legal standing. Both lived on Willapa Bay, and each had oyster farms that could suffer direct harm from the spraying. The science, and their own observations, indicated that carbaryl was a toxin; that it was contaminating their oyster beds; and that it likely causes cancer and other serious health effects. Edward Cohen, Fritzi's husband, was not party to the appeal because he had just died from cancer.

The Willapa Coalitions' appeal argued, "On the whole, Ecology's decision to issue the NPDES Permit constitutes an erroneous interpretation of state and federal law and is a clearly erroneous application of the law to facts. And is not supported by evidence that is substantial when viewed in light of the whole record before the Department."

It was that simple: carbaryl was indisputably toxic. The Willapa Coalitions argued that it was so toxic that the Shellfish Association couldn't meet the water quality standards, even with Ecology's liberal testing delays to allow for dilution. They argued that the Shellfish Association would not likely meet the Sediment Quality standards either, which didn't allow for this type of pollution—standards that Ecology kept delaying from being implemented. The Willapa Coalitions concluded that the federal permit to spray carbaryl was against the law.

SMOKING EMAIL

The Appellants found this email, written by Ecology's permit writer, which exposed the backstory:

> The other matter put to Senator Snyder was sediment study. I left this out of the first two versions because there is some confusion about the checklist in our permit writer's manual. I received hints from WTC (Washington Toxics Coalition) that they thought (t)his was an important omission, so I checked further. Bret Betts in sediments was aggressively hostile to my inquiry, but Roger Dovel is being helpful. I believe this is the Achilles heel for the growers, since the burrowing shrimp temporary modification exemption never made it to the Sediment regs. I warned the growers of this at their workshop on the 27th. They became angry and would not listen. To them, every question is politically driven. They believe that an impersonal law impartially enforced is an impossible concept.
>
> The last thing they object to is further study in the Schedule of Compliance to determine eventual AKART by next renewal. Even though they agreed on this provision in the previous MOA, they have decided that they will defy everyone.
>
> Let's consider the growers position on this permit as a whole, rather than objection by detail. They want a permit without fee, limits, monitoring, or a schedule of compliance. They got the first two; they are striving for a complete victory. Without these four items, a permit is meaningless. I believe they will lose in court. They don't care. They have Senator Snyder who will protect them forever.

As if swatting at an annoying insect, the state attorney assigned to represent Ecology tried to persuade the Board to dismiss the Willapa Coalitions' appeal of the Ecology carbaryl permit.

He wrote:

> In what has become an annual ritual, the Ad Hoc Coalition
> for Willapa Bay ... has appealed and requests a stay of the
> permit issued by the Department of Ecology to the Shellfish
> Association, for the use of carbaryl to control burrowing
> shrimp populations. In the past, these appeals have been
> summarily dismissed by the Board either on procedural
> grounds or for lack of evidence.

But not this time. The Board did not dismiss the case, and it was headed for a hearing on April 23, 2003.

The state attorney, under Christine Gregoire's leadership, was ramped up to defend state approval of carbaryl spraying into what was once one of the most biologically productive coastal estuaries in Washington State.

Instead, on April 28, 2003, the Willapa Coalitions and the Shellfish Association came to an out-of-court Settlement Agreement.

They began discussions in December of 2002, and by March 2003, had an agreement in principle to settle their differences. The use of carbaryl to kill shrimp on Willapa Bay and Grays Harbor would be terminated ... but not for another **ten years.** It would cease in December 2012.

So the growers received another decade of guaranteed spraying. In the meantime, the Shellfish Association had to reduce the total amount of carbaryl used—from the 6,400 pounds per year, by 10 percent in 2003, 20 percent in 2004, and then by 30 percent for the years 2005 to 2012. For the final eight years of this plan, only 4,480 pounds per year could be sprayed, down from 6,400 pounds.

To ensure that these reductions were met, the Willapa Coalitions demanded monitoring and certification by Agriculture, a long-standing proponent of pesticide use.

The Shellfish Association also agreed to research alternative shrimp control and oyster culture methods, with an annual contribution of $10,000 for each of the remaining three years of the federal permit that the Willapa Coalitions had appealed. This research was to focus on alternative shrimp control methods, and only allowed research on products that were exempt from EPA registration, things like cedar wood oil, castor oil, cinnamon oil, or citric acid.

Finally, the Willapa Coalitions negotiated an optional requirement that the Shellfish Association make a good faith effort to further reduce and cease the use of carbaryl in advance of the 2012 deadline.

Only time would tell if the Shellfish Association used this conflict as a transformative experience. With this permit challenge and negotiated settlement, the larger community concerns and preferences provided guideposts that they could choose to adopt or resist. Would the Shellfish Association move forward using sustainable farming methods and forego the use of chemicals? Would they adopt practices that supported their claims that their oysters were raised in pristine waters using sustainable practices and responsible farming techniques? Would they adjust their financial bottom line motivations and accept a likely lower production of the non-native oyster that was in balance with the space required by the native shrimp?

With the hope that the Shellfish Association would give up its predilection for pesticides, the Willapa Coalitions dropped their appeal of the Ecology-issued federal permit.

Chapter 13: Gentle Touch?

Fritzi and Edward Cohen first came to Willapa Bay in the 1980s on the advice of the *Best Places* guide for the Pacific Northwest. They were on an extended holiday from Washington D.C., where Fritzi had just completed a fundraising project for the Washington Moscow Capital Citizens Exchange, on which she served as President.

Long Beach peninsula sounded like a funky place, and they fell in love with the area. "We came here to recover and were sitting at a seafood restaurant in Nahcotta, when we saw this historical inn for sale," Fritzi recalled in an interview for this book. "The inn wasn't operating because the owners were elderly and had no children; they couldn't keep up. It had been on the market for five years. The place was decrepit, but we made a down payment on it anyhow, then came back in the winter to see what it was like then. We bought it in 1988. The inn was built in 1929 and the property included tidelands. We were totally in heaven," Fritzi said.

The inn had enjoyed a varied and storied existence, including housing the U.S. Coast Guard Horse Patrol during World War II, making it a tourist attraction and historical site of significant import in Pacific County.

Not knowing the Cohens from Adam, the Shellfish Association

appealed the Pacific County permits necessary to re-open the historic inn. "This didn't make sense," Fritzi said. "The area was depressed, and an inn could help the local economy. Why would they oppose us re-opening this inn?"

The inn had been operating as a commercial venture since 1929, prior to land use laws and zoning. But Pacific County adopted zoning in 1981, and the new zoning did not allow for a commercial establishment, even though the inn was already there. Before they were able to open for business, the Cohens had to secure approvals that would allow them to re-open the inn, serve food, and expand the size of the main building to enlarge the guest rooms. Their first step was to correct the zoning, which required an application to Pacific County Board of County Commissioners, who granted the rezone in 1989 despite Shellfish Association opposition. Pacific County issued their building permits.

"We tried to make sense of all this," Fritzi said, as if it had happened yesterday. "For some reason, they didn't want the inn to be operational."

The Cohens lovingly restored the buildings and decorated the interior in the spirit of the 1930s with non-matching furnishings that set it apart from the chain hotels. It was a boutique hotel before the term was coined. A stay at the inn came with a full breakfast featuring oysters from the tidelands, organic vegetables, herbs, and flowers.

Their daughter joined them in the endeavor, and their neighbor, Larry Warnberg, started showing them how to farm oysters using organic methods. "The oysters were abundant and we didn't know then they were non-native, not that I would have cared. We considered them a gift of nature. Edward didn't care for the oysters, but I LOVED them," Fritzi reminisced.

After winning Round 1, the battle to correct the zoning, they opened the Inn in 1990 for lodging and meals. In addition, they invested in a shoreline permit to expand and modernize in the near future. Pacific County and Ecology granted that permit as well.

Shortly after they opened—to their shock and dismay—guests were sitting out on the waterfront and saw a helicopter spraying something. They wanted to know more, but the Cohens had no idea what the spray was for, or why it was spraying near their property. There had been no indication about the carbaryl spraying on the property deed or title, nor was there direct notice to the Cohens as tideland property owners and organic oyster growers. The day the helicopter came to spray the carbaryl was the day the Cohens started a long journey to keep chemicals out of Willapa Bay, and specifically, off their property. Their efforts to stop the spraying began in the early 1990s and weren't limited to just carbaryl: they were opposed to any pesticide use in Willapa Bay. As one might expect, they suspended serving oysters during the height of the spray program.

In the meantime, their plans for the inn changed and they were required to go back and modify the original approvals granted in 1990 before they could proceed. Pacific County granted their request.

In Round 2, the second odd thing was when the Shellfish Association appealed the Cohen's Pacific County approved re-zone amendment to the Pacific County Superior Court, which granted the appeal and determined that the zoning was inconsistent with the surrounding properties.

The Shellfish Association also appealed the shoreline permit granted by Pacific County in 2000. Their appeal was heard by the state Shoreline Hearings Board, and denied.

Not dissuaded, the Shellfish Association pressed the matter further by filing a lawsuit to challenge the denial of its appeal of the Cohens' shoreline permit. In dueling lawsuits, the Cohens simultaneously filed a lawsuit challenging the superior court decision that their long-standing re-zone was now a spot zone. The two lawsuits were consolidated into one hearing, and the state appeals court ruled in favor of the Cohens and the inn, in both matters. The court agreed with Pacific County and found that operation of the historical inn did not alter the rural character of the area, as the Shellfish Association had argued. The court upheld the state's revised shoreline permit.

The Cohens wondered: who were these members of the Shellfish Association? Although the membership of the Shellfish Association fluctuates over time, ninety-five percent of its members are shellfish companies in Willapa Bay and Grays Harbor, people that the Cohens didn't know well, and most they'd never met.

"It was all very bizarre when this group came after us like they did. Another member of the Shellfish Association told us they owned the inn's tidelands, but that it hadn't been legally recorded," Fritzi said, then added, "By that time, we realized we'd gotten ourselves into a hornet's nest of local politics. If we had known that the Shellfish Association was going to attack us for simply existing, and about the farming practices on Willapa Bay, and the character of the sprayers, we would never have bought this property."

SHELLFISH ASSOCIATION'S MISSION

According to Shellfish Association materials, the organization is a "…non-profit group dedicated to the production of oysters and other shellfish in an environmentally and economically sustainable manner." And that it "contributes substantially to the preservation of the estuary and its pristine water quality in many ways, including the eradication of the invasive cordgrass, spartina."

How did protesting the operation of an existing inn with a modest planned expansion fit into the mission of the Shellfish Association? This was the same Shellfish Association that had, by that time, been spraying a neurotoxic pesticide directly into the bay for more than thirty years, with massive animal casualties and ecosystem impacts that were beyond state quantification. How could the re-opening of an established nine-room inn affect the alleged pristine water quality? And if by some remote chance that it did, for instance due to a failing septic drainfield, how could that come near what the Shellfish Association was doing?

Since the Shellfish Association's objections to the inn ratcheted up in 1999 and 2000 after the Cohens became active to stop the annual carbaryl spraying and to stop the use of more chemicals to eradicate spartina, Fritzi suspects that the real reason for the second round against them was because their actions came in direct conflict with the *other* part of the Shellfish Association's mission: production of oysters. "We felt like we were retaliated against for voicing our concerns and filing appeals to get this madness stopped," Fritzi said.

In an attempt to shed light on some of the oyster farmer's behavior, retired Ecology manager Steve Saunders said that from their perspective, they are no different from upland farming. "They see what they are doing as aquaculture farming. They equate spraying pesticides into the aquatic environment to boost productivity on par with terrestrial farming's use of pesticides. The purpose of farming in water and upland is to eliminate pests and boost productivity. That's their argument. But this is different. These are waters of the nation and the state, and a completely different setting than terrestrial farming," Saunders said.

It's Your Problem

From the oyster farmer's point of view, it was a "taking" of their land if they lost productivity due to the native burrowing shrimp. Under the takings clause of the U.S. constitution, private property shall not be taken for public use, without just compensation. The argument went like this: the shellfish companies must be justly compensated if their privately owned tidelands were "taken" for public use. Habitat for burrowing shrimp, in this case, was public use. The shellfish companies argued that it was the state's responsibility to step in and control the burrowing shrimp, which, they argued, were a problem for the entire ecosystem, and they were bearing the brunt of this societal problem.

Tim Smith made this argument clear when speaking at the Burrowing Shrimp meeting convened by Senator Snyder in 1993:

> I am the Executive Director of the Pacific Coast Shellfish Growers Association... The shrimp infestation is occurring on privately held, privately titled tidelands in most situations ... but if this were, say, Scotch broom, and the lot next to you was publicly owned, and it was blowing onto your property, you would go and ask the owner to control Scotch broom on his lot so it wasn't impacting the use of your property... I am a little reluctant to keep restating this as the industry's problem because somehow the focus has shifted from controlling burrowing shrimp in the estuary to controlling burrowing shrimp on these privately held tidelands.
>
> The industry has certainly paid the cost out of lost production, and I get a call about once a month from some attorney in the state somewhere who calls up just to remind me that they think there is a "taking" issue involved. But if we can keep the focus on the role of the burrowing shrimp in the estuary and the need to try to address that, I think we can all go a lot further and keep moving towards this. And really, it puts the responsibility, I think, to broaden the perspective more directly on the agencies to try to do something to solve this problem instead of trying to figure out what the industry can or cannot do to address really a fairly small percentage of the overall problem....

An oyster company owner, with a hand in drafting various

carbaryl environmental documents, echoed this argument, "…I agree, Tim, it was very well put, that this is a bay problem and it is a biological problem—the shrimp are choking the bay—the oystermen just happen to be working on a portion of it and we cannot work with the shrimp. The agencies should not be able to stand the shrimp being there, and we have to point it out."

Indeed, in 2002, the Shellfish Association filed a document as part of the Willapa Coalitions appeal making this same argument: if not allowed to spray, the land is useless and a liability instead of an asset, and the Shellfish Association would be aggrieved and adversely affected by any suspension or delay in the ability to spray carbaryl onto the shrimp.

~

Many people have tried to stem the tide of pesticide use. When Rachel Carson wrote *Silent Spring* in 1962, she raised public awareness about the effects of pesticide use on our health and environment. However, in the almost sixty years since Carson drew attention to the health and environmental impacts of DDT, use of equally hazardous pesticides has only increased. And more evidence is surfacing all the time that human exposure to pesticides is linked to health problems.

For example, in May 2010, scientists from the University of Montreal and Harvard University released a study that found exposure to pesticide residues on vegetables and fruit may double a child's risk of attention deficit hyperactivity disorder, a condition that can cause inattention, hyperactivity, and impulsivity in children. "We are drowning our world in untested and unsafe chemicals and the price we are paying in terms of our reproductive health is of serious concern," stated Gian Carlo Di Renzo, a physician and lead author of an International Federation of Gynecology and Obstetrics report released in 2015.

Pesticides are used in our schools, parks, and public lands. Pesticides are sprayed on agricultural fields and wood lots. Pesticides can be found in our air, food, soil, water and even in our breast milk. And pesticides are found in oysters.

Pesticides can cause many types of cancer in humans. Some of the most prevalent forms include: leukemia, non-Hodgkins lymphoma, and brain, bone, breast, ovarian, prostate, testicular, and liver cancers. Children who live in homes where their parents use pesticides are twice as likely to develop brain cancer versus those who live in residences in which no pesticides are used.

Studies by the National Cancer Institute found that American farmers, who in most respects are healthier than the population at large, had startling incidences of leukemia, Hodgkins disease, non-Hodgkins lymphoma, and many other forms of cancer.

Evidence is mounting that exposure to pesticides disrupts the endocrine system, wreaking havoc with the complex regulation of hormones, the reproductive system, and embryonic development. Endocrine disruption can produce infertility and a variety of birth defects and developmental defects in offspring, including hormonal imbalance and incomplete sexual development, impaired brain development, behavioral disorders, and numerous others. Examples of known endocrine disrupting chemicals which are present in large quantities in our environment include DDT (which persisted in abundance for more than twenty years after being banned in the U.S.), lindane, atrazine, carbaryl, parathion, etc. From this list, lindane and carbaryl have both been used in Willapa Bay—carbaryl much more extensively.

The Cohens were keenly aware of the dangers of pesticides and this motivated them to try to stop use of pesticides in the waters surrounding their property. Edward Cohen died in 1999 from multiple myeloma, a rare form of cancer of the bone marrow plasma cells, essential to protect the body from infection. Multiple myeloma affects a relatively small population of 200,000 people per year. "It was a terrible disease," is all Fritzi would say about that time of her life. Symptoms include low blood cell count, anemia, fatigue, weakness, pale complexion, easy bleeding and bruising, bone pain, weak and easily broken bones, infections, plus kidney damage and failure.

Initially they fought the use of glyphosate, then carbaryl. But when he was diagnosed, Edward's wellbeing took priority. Fritzi wrote a friend explaining her absence in the pesticide wars. "This was a tough time for me. My husband, Edward, was in the last throes of multiple myeloma. He died Nov. 3, 1999."

Fritzi returned to her fight against the use of chemicals in Willapa Bay, without Edward. On top of appeal expenses, she was losing money from her tideland farm. Fritzi provided oysters to two restaurants in Portland, but stopped in 2007 when she found out her property had received chemical drift. "I was in negotiations to provide oysters to a seafood distributor in Santa Fe, but after I positively knew that my oysters were exposed to pesticides, I broke off the conversation. When I complained locally, other growers suggested that I just not tell anyone." Fritzi concluded, "There was no way that I would do that."

In 2009, she won a court case and the right to control spartina on her property by mowing and pulling it by hand (instead of spraying with glyphosate and imazapyr, covered in the next chapter). The inn co-manager, Keith Stavrum, mowed and cut the spartina. He was soon diagnosed with non-Hodgkins lymphoma and underwent chemotherapy. The disease went into remission, but came back in 2015.

Non-Hodgkins lymphoma is associated with exposure to radiation, cancer-causing chemicals, or infections. People who are exposed to weed and insect pesticides are also at higher risk for this type of cancer.

A representative of a shellfish company owner that sprays pesticides is the voice-over in *Willapa Bay Oysters*, which shows a helicopter spraying the tideflats—but with no explanation. Instead, she says, "I know sometimes we have problems with outsiders that may not agree with some of the things we do here, but I think they have to understand the culture and the community and the process of the whole thing and understand that the oyster growers here have the water quality as their best interest." Yet the spewing helicopter is not explained. There's no mention of carbaryl, burrowing shrimp, or the 10-plus million animals killed yearly.

PROTEST FATIGUE

Fritzi fought for the environment, and spent thousands of hours at hearings, meetings, researching, writing letters, and rallying others to join the war. Plus thousands of her own dollars. She nursed Edward as he coped with an awful disease, and she continues to support her partner through another form of cancer—wondering what role pesticide use on Willapa played in her personal misfortunes, and how she might have contributed to her loved ones' exposure to chemicals.

Fritzi summed it all up in an interview with Lindsay Dahl: "The politicians in Washington State, no matter what their political affiliation, have supported the spraying of chemicals in the waters of Washington State because of the aquaculture industry. Currently, there is an effort to curtail the ability of citizens to protest the permits that are required for spraying into the waters, which are covered by the Clean Water Act. This effort is happening all over the West Coast, and is being supported by the U.S. Congress."

Fritzi's partner, Stavrum, says Fritzi is referred to by some opponents as "that Jew Bitch from New York." But she says this doesn't bother her. Fritzi bats her eyes, gives a Gallic shrug, and says with an east coast accent, "I'm not from New York. I'm from Wis-CON-sin."

Fritzi says she is tired of fighting. She's tired of fighting with Pacific County. She's tired of fighting with WSU. She's tired of fighting Ecology. She's tired of the politicians who she believes cut private deals that destroy the environment. She's had it with the shellfish companies that, from her point of view, are addicted to pesticides. All insist that pesticide use is safe, which doesn't jive with her personal experience or knowledge. Perhaps most of all, she's frustrated and saddened with a community that didn't cover her back as she valiantly attempted to stop the use of pesticides in Willapa Bay.

Not surprisingly, she said, "I no longer feel a real sense of commitment to this community or its well-being."

The Warnbergs

Dear Martha:

Image by Lola Pallardy

Life is still blissful paradise here in Nahcotta, on Willapa Bay. Except for the death threats. Not that we expect anybody to really follow through, but vigilante justice is not unknown here.

Larry Warnberg was the target for many forms of vigilante justice in the bucolic Willapa Bay community. Since he got around almost exclusively by bicycle, he became an easy target on the road. "Fortunately, I have a mirror, saw them coming, hit the ditch, and lived to tell the tale. No question about their identity—their vehicles were quite familiar in our small community," Larry said.

"Why would the sprayers resort to violence?" Larry pondered. "Because the average oyster lover couldn't protest their pesticide use since they didn't have legal standing. As a licensed grower, I had standing. To stop our litigation efforts, their initial strategy was to force me out of business. There were several attempts to buy me out, which I politely declined. Then the serious pressure was applied. Dead chickens were placed on my bunk in our live-aboard sailboat; my dog, Muttley, was poisoned; and complaints about me concerning spurious violations were lodged with numerous government agencies. I was investigated thoroughly by bureaucrats sent to put me out of business, including County officials, several State agents, the IRS, and FDA. None found any violation. I maintained my license and pursued the litigation that successfully resulted in a phase-out of carbaryl. Since I lived on a boat, they thought they could get me on waste discharges. First, they sent the county septic inspector to shut me down, claiming that I was dumping stuff into the bay. I had a composting toilet and gray water system. They couldn't find anything wrong. Then they sent a Washington State Department of Health inspector to my farm. This person understood that she was being manipulated. She didn't find anything wrong. So then, they turned the IRS on me. And one day, an inspector from the FDA shows up unannounced. I'd never seen a federal inspector before. He found film on my worktable. But since I didn't ship oysters to Astoria, which was out of state, he had no jurisdiction and the guy left, although he seemed quite eager to write me up."

Larry makes light of the harsh treatment he received during those years. "Both the Cohens and me endured a lot of pressure to stop the litigation, but we kept on and survived. There's no need to dwell on it. We have moved on."

Larry sold oysters for many years to a seafood shop in nearby

Ocean Park. The shop was owned by two older women. "One day I delivered the bi-weekly order as usual, but one of the ladies broke down in tears and said she couldn't buy from me anymore, or else she would be forced out of business because the suppliers of crab, clams, and shucked oysters would cut her off. The Growers tried the same tactic with the owner of a restaurant I supplied, and when they did, the owner told that bully to never show his face again in her restaurant. She was one of the few individuals willing to stand up for me," he said with admiration.

In the meantime, Larry kept demonstrating that oysters could be successfully grown without pesticides, albeit on a smaller scale than the big companies wanted. And he kept drawing attention to the spraying.

"Around 1998, the Executive Director of the Pacific Coast Shellfish Growers Association, persuaded me to join and then oversaw my ex-communication. Up until that time, I had boycotted it for many years due to their support of carbaryl spraying. I wasn't a member for long before I was kicked out for writing a Letter to the Editor of our local newspaper in which I criticized a prominent oyster farmer. I said he was something of a mercenary fat cat who sprayed the Bay with poison while driving his Mercedes on the backs of underpaid Mexican workers. The Association didn't approve and said they didn't like my 'confrontational methods.' The Board was dominated by the sprayers and there was no room in the tent for my opposition to spraying."

During that contentious time, an oyster farmer to the north of Larry's lease got as close as he possibly could to Larry's oysters with a backpack sprayer.

Fritzi recalled that event as well, "They sprayed right along Larry's property line. It was so obviously blatant."

Larry Warnberg was in good company. The tactics used against him were the same tactics used against people trying to prevent the use of DDT; the pesticide Larry had been exposed to before his bone cancer.

Fifty years ago, a few brave scientists and an attorney filed a lawsuit in Suffolk County, Long Island, to end the spraying of DDT, a pesticide that was killing fish and birds in Long Island's marshes. Their battle cry was, "Sue the bastards!" According to an Environmental Defense Fund's newsletter, on August 14, 1966, a judge issued a temporary injunction that stopped the spraying. The next day—amazingly—a truck rolled down the streets and sprayed DDT on the front yard of the attorney. The judge was irate, and the DDT advocates lost credibility. Those same scientists and attorney went on to incorporate the national Environmental Defense Fund the next year, and led the nationwide fight to ban the use of DDT in the United States in 1972.

"It appeared to me to be a deliberate move to contaminate my beds. I got the DFW shellfish biologist, stationed at the Nahcotta Shellfish Laboratory, to come and witness the die-off on my tideland lease, which he did," Larry said. "As a result, I didn't have oysters for six months. The state staff left the samples taken from my plot in their fridge for six months and finally sent them off to a lab in Yakima. The sample results came back positive for carbaryl. But because they had sat in the fridge for so long, they said that the results were not valid. The staff at the shellfish lab supported the carbaryl program," Larry added, as a possible explanation for behavior that was harmful to his business.

Ultimately, Larry was forced out of business because he did not own his own land. He relied on a lease with his former partner's widow, and a lease with the Port of Peninsula. "The next move was to force me off the five-acre lease in front of my former partner's house where I had been farming successfully sixteen years."

Larry also leased five acres of tideland from the Port of Peninsula, a public agency, "The sprayers that didn't like my efforts to stop their use of pesticides tried to get the Port Commissioners to not renew my lease. Lease renewals were typically a routine matter of business, however, the Commission held an unusual Executive Session when considering my renewal application. They emerged from a confidential discussion with their attorney and voted to renew my lease. I was still in business," Larry said.

GENTLE POISONING

Not only did some shellfish companies believe that if they couldn't control the native shrimp (ideally, the state would do it) and that the presence of the native burrowing shrimp was a "taking" of their property, but that carbaryl had a "light touch." They argued that carbaryl's touch was gentle when compared to other measures to eradicate the shrimp. Use of carbaryl was, therefore, justifiable. An early Burrowing Shrimp Committee chairman, Jim Walls, wrote, "At least for the present, carbaryl seems to be the lightest touch to control a pest that threatens the industry's ability to be profitable."

(Just to re-cap: carbaryl is toxic to the touch; can kill anything with a nervous system (from fleas to humans); is considered a warfare agent; is toxic to invertebrates and vertebrates; kills shrimp, fish, clams, crab, worms, and microscopic floating animals called zooplankton, which are at "the bottom of the food chain"; causes cardiac arrest in fish embryos; causes mutations; causes tumors in mice; is likely cancerous to humans; and has other non-fatal adverse impacts such as slowed growth in clams, etc).

A prominent shellfish company owner and sprayer echoed the concept of gentle poisoning. "I would rather have the gentle touch of a particular chemical, than the harsh reality of some mechanical means or something to destroy a problem," he said at the 1993 Sid

Snyder Burrowing Shrimp Meeting. "In what we're doing, we are really trying to probably correct the mistakes people in the past Department of Fisheries administrations have created. We are trying to come back on an explosive bunch of shrimp that are out of control... The research was done... These studies showed that the oyster industry ... has a positive impact on the protection of young crab. So yes, sometimes a chemical is a good way to deal with things. So, the problem, Senator, is not science. The problem is politics."

Larry Warnberg has a different reality. "In 2006, I was diagnosed with stage 3 colon cancer, went through surgery and chemotherapy... still living to tell about it. I never claim the cancer was due to carbaryl, arsenic, or other common toxins. Correlation doesn't mean causation. There are plenty of reasons to resist waste and pollution without invoking personal suspicions."

CHAPTER 14: SPARTINA

Fox News was the background to the smell of gun oil and final chambering as Marcial Hunter cleaned his shotgun. An avid duck hunter, Marcial owns property on Willapa Bay and retired there in 2002. The family property includes tidelands, and he hunts on his land as well as in other parts of Willapa Bay. But he doesn't just kill birds. He examines them like a mortician doing forensics, conducting autopsies to learn what the now-dead birds had been eating. As a retired nuclear engineer with a degree in Naval Science and a second major in oceanography, Marcial has a deep appreciation for scientific methods and thorough research. This approach reflects his personality—patient, thorough, inquiring, with a wry sense of humor.

Marcial, Ralph, and their younger brother, Miles, had an idyllic childhood. They'd grown up in southwestern Oregon in a cabin with no electricity on eighty acres. During his early years, the whole family focused on putting food on the table. Because his parents were Great Depression survivors, the kids learned early that nothing went to waste. Everything was appreciated and valued. Along with this survival instinct came a curiosity about the natural world, and an appreciation for education. Marcial's mother was gregarious, and worked as a registered nurse at the hospital in Roseburg. His father was a nature lover and a skilled hunter and fisherman. He taught his sons to hunt and fish, mainly for food. Oddly, his father couldn't eat some of the animals they killed saying, "I can't eat my friends."

At home, the bird books and the shotgun were always at hand. While at Boy Scout camp, Marcial was eventually not allowed to answer the plant or animal identification quizzes because he always knew all the answers. Luckily, he also competed in high

Image by Lola Pallardy

school track, which humbled him because no matter how good he was and no matter what level he reached, someone always beat him.

His father served in World War II as an officer in naval intelligence in Panama. Later, he got a job as a biology teacher at Myrtle Creek High School. Marcial helped him trap birds for banding, and they trapped squirrels for use in his biology class. It wasn't until Marcial hunted ducks for the first time that he got hooked on hunting. At first, it bothered him tremendously to kill animals, especially the rabbits, but he says he got over it.

Marcial's worldview, which is informed by data, facts, and analysis for drawing logical conclusions, stands in stark contrast to the political management of Willapa Bay, Marcial's home. Conflict was inevitable.

In 2002, Marcial wasn't following the Willapa Coalitions' lawsuit or the subsequent settlement with the Shellfish Association regarding carbaryl. He didn't even know Larry Warnberg or Fritzi Cohen. But he was reluctantly involved in the spraying of other chemicals in

Willapa Bay: the herbicides intended to kill the spartina that had been introduced by the shellfish companies in the late 1800s.

Spartina is native to the East Coast and can commonly be seen there, bending in the wind on sandy meadows between estuaries winding toward the sea. Spartina is prized on the eastern coastline for acting as a natural erosion buffer, filtering pollution from water and gathering nutrients. But state agencies, conservation groups, shellfish companies, and others on the West Coast consider spartina a dangerous alien invader that threatens native habitats by dominating tidal mudflats in areas like Willapa Bay.

Spartina was brought to Willapa Bay in 1894 along with the eastern oysters the oyster companies hoped would replace the Olympia oysters they had extirpated by overharvest and habitat destruction, and it spread from there to Grays Harbor, likely by seed. The plant overtakes mudflats when introduced to new areas, and as it spreads and grows, it traps sediments, creating meadows.

The net effect of spartina on the West Coast was a gradual change of mudflats into salt marshes, and according to Agriculture, was considered to be a major threat to the "huge commercial shellfish industry that is extremely important to the economy," even though the oysters they farmed on the mudflats were also non-native invasive species.

Spartina displaced other native species, including burrowing shrimp, and was capable of altering the land's physical structure. Some of the sediment carried into clumps of spartina on the tide was trapped there and, over time, meadows rose above the mud. Meadows of beautiful, monoculture grass. At spartina's peak in 2003, about 8,000 acres of Willapa Bay tideflats were covered with spartina, forming the largest meadows in the state. But there was more to the story than what met the eye because the plant had been in the bay for more than half a century without becoming a problem. Something had changed. Spartina in Willapa Bay was identified in 1940, but it wasn't until the 1980s that it began to draw increasingly more and more attention with its rapidly accelerating spread.

MAKE UP YOUR MIND

The Shellfish Association, which had long argued that the tideflats inhabited by shrimp were dead zones, and therefore okay to poison with carbaryl, now found itself defending the ecological functions of these same tideflats as the spartina took over what they had previously been referring to as "vacant land."

Willapa Bay is a major stopover for migratory birds in the spring and summer—it's "on the map" as a rest stop along what is called the Pacific Flyway. Each year, at least a billion birds migrate from Alaska to Patagonia along the Pacific Flyway, but these birds are only a fraction of those that used the flyway a century ago. Out of those billion birds, up to one million of them stop to feed in the mudflats of Willapa Bay. When their numbers started to decline in 1991, spartina was blamed.

An oft-touted concern with the spread of spartina was the loss of duckgrass (botanical name *Zostera japonica*, also called eelgrass). Of the two species of eelgrass present in Willapa Bay, duckgrass occupies the upper tideflats that were being overtaken by spartina.

Because duckgrass is exposed on low tides or in shallow water, both the blades and the roots are accessible to the migratory waterfowl, especially ducks. That's why it's called duckgrass. Ducks, and two species of geese, eat duckgrass. And some of these ducks and geese ended up in the sights of Marcial's shotgun, and then, a few hours later, on his operating table.

During their long migration, every calorie is critical. Birds are particularly vulnerable and die if they do not find food at each traditional layover along their extraordinary journeys.

The other eelgrass, *marina*, is also critical for the migratory birds. While it is present in the upper inter-tidal zone, *marina* prefers the cooler, deeper waters (much like the Olympia oyster), and is not as accessible.

Agriculture and the Shellfish Association used the threat of losing the non-native duckgrass to justify eradication of the spartina that appeared to be taking over duckgrass' part of the tideland and turning it into meadows. As hard as this may be to follow, within the next few years, the Shellfish Association then determined that this same valuable duckgrass conflicted with its mono-crop farming of another non-native invasive species: manila clams, one of the most lucrative shellfish products worldwide, and mounted yet another successful pesticide campaign, this time to eradicate the duckgrass. This part of the story is covered in the last chapter.

Throughout the 1990s, spartina began to invade new territory at an alarming rate. Calls for an immediate control effort came from the shellfish companies, an industry valued at $16.4 million in 1993, whose concerns were supported by others including the fishing industry, biologists, government agencies, and members of the Willapa community.

Not everyone agreed that spartina's impacts were adverse, and there were documented concerns about both the anti-spartina study methodologies and their results. That aspect of the spartina story is not explored in depth in this book.

Estuary On Drugs

All this talk about spraying spartina and putting yet another pesticide into Willapa Bay and Grays Harbor came right on the heels of the 1992 carbaryl environmental documents that called for yet more study, breaking news about the Shoalwaters' infant mortality crisis, and concerns about environmental toxins.

Marcial remained in the background as the first few steps were taken by the state in the late 1980s and early 1990s. Besides, he didn't yet live full-time on Willapa Bay.

First, in 1993, the state formed a Spartina Working Group, followed by listing spartina as a class of noxious weed that required mandatory eradication, culminating in the issuance of a plan to manage spartina as an invasive aquatic plant species. Since the state's aquatic invasive plant guidelines required an integrated pest management approach, this meant evaluating a variety of control methods like mowing, mulching, and biological controls. But chemicals soon become the primary weapon against spartina.

Marcial kept close watch on Willapa Bay. He believed spartina was displacing key elements of the local food web, and thought it needed to be controlled. If control included the appropriate application of chemicals, that was okay with him.

Operations to eradicate spartina began slowly in 1994, and by 1996, had ramped up to include large-scale eradication methods of mowing, then mowing and applying herbicides, then applying herbicides, and then seedling removal. But none of these approaches could keep up with the spread of the plant. The state and federal agencies with public land management responsibilities on Willapa Bay pooled resources to eradicate the spartina. Even so, their efforts could focus only on 10 percent of the area covered with spartina, while the remainder continued to spread.

"By 1995, the oyster growers felt things were moving too slow with Ecology in the lead, so they got their State Senator, Sid Snyder, to pass a bill to take authority for this task away from Ecology and hand it to Agriculture. The law gave Agriculture the lead on destruction."

And as Marcial—the former nuclear plant operator--wryly noted in an interview for this book said, "If you want something nuked even worse than what Ecology can do, Agriculture is the place to go."

Not only was Agriculture now the lead on destroying spartina, it was also tasked with registering all pesticides for use in Washington State, after EPA registration. Accordingly, Agriculture, with its expertise in upland agriculture pesticides, facilitated the cooperation of local, state, federal, and tribal governments; universities; interest groups; and private landowners, to eradicate spartina in Washington State. On Willapa Bay, Marcial observed the formation of what he calls a pecking order, "The Willapa National Wildlife Refuge was at the top, the local WSU extension agent in the middle, and the Pacific County Noxious Weed Control Board was at the bottom."

The reason the plant was a problem is because a clump of spartina develops a huge root mass—so big it inspired all manner of metaphor: the size of a VW Bug; the size of a young elephant, etc. The roots are very, very, large. When spreading as a rhizome, the plant appears as tiny sprouts, but if the sprout survives, it becomes a clone. Marcial said, "It may take years for it to reach the size of a kitchen, and then it seems to explode."

MONSANTO

The Monsanto Company (Monsanto) swooped in to save Willapa Bay from spartina with its patented pesticides. Willapa Bay made it on the front page of Monsanto's company magazine in 1991, and was featured in an article titled, "No Time To Lose: Will Rodeo Save Willapa Bay?" The company was scoping out the bay as a potential market for Rodeo, the aquatic version of the company's popular herbicide Roundup, their brand name for glyphosate. Some critics of spraying glyphosate, including Fritzi Cohen, believe Monsanto demonizes invasive species like spartina in order to develop a new market for its chemicals. "They figured if they could spray (Rodeo) in a pristine bay, they could spray it anywhere," Fritzi said, "Spartina grows in many areas across the world where it is considered non-native. If Rodeo proved effective for eradicating spartina from Willapa Bay, Monsanto could establish new markets in coastal areas from New Zealand to Europe."

Larry and Fritzi argued that spartina was a symptom of an eco-system out of balance from too much silt, a result of clear-cut logging, road construction, oyster dredging; and too many nutrients from agricultural run-off, sewage outfalls, and leaky septic systems. Larry wrote in an Op-Ed for the local paper, "An ounce of prevention is worth thousands of gallons of herbicide, but it's hard to sell prevention, and herbicide is highly profitable ($125/gal). Treating symptoms with a short-term chemical fix is the culturally sanctioned approach to complex problems. Monsanto becomes the beneficiary as a consequence of society's limited attention span."

In 1994, permits for glyphosate were issued, and three groups including the Ad Hoc Coalition for Willapa Bay, filed appeals. A joint hearing of the appeals was scheduled for December before the Board and the Shoreline Hearings Board, for which the Washington Chapter of the Nature Conservancy was providing legal defense *against* the citizen appeals. The appellants and the state avoided the hearing and reached a settlement allowing limited spraying but with careful monitoring, and chemical control was to be the least preferred method.

But their settlement was unacceptable to the Nature Conservancy, its local Willapa Alliance, and to Monsanto. Senator Snyder introduced emergency legislation nullifying the settlement, eliminated most permit requirements, required no monitoring, and appropriated $1.5 million for glyphosate use—a drop in the bucket for the eventual $30+ million public expense for the spartina eradication program.

Seeing the Nature Conservancy sitting next to Monsanto defending the use of herbicides was a shock for Steve Saunders when he worked for Ecology, but poisoning invasive plants is one of their ecosystem management tools. In 2001, the Nature Conservancy, which owns land in Willapa Bay that it says it is protecting, published their weed control handbook, which covers "appropriate" herbicide use in four of its eight chapters.

Not only was the settlement agreement unacceptable to Monsanto and the Nature Conservancy, Monsanto had a seat at the table, sitting right next to Senator Sid Snyder when drafting the successful legislative language in meetings. "Anyone opposed to the use of pesticides in Willapa Bay was up against the oyster growers, Senator Sid Snyder, and Monsanto, a pretty formidable group," Saunders recalled.

In spite of the opposition to large-scale pesticide application of another chemical into the Willapa Bay ecosystem, there was a flood of public money dedicated to eradicating spartina, with coordination among the state, shellfish industry, tribes, and environmental organizations including the Nature Conservancy. The Nature Conservancy says it works to protect the habitat and water quality of Willapa Bay, but there is no record of any Nature Conservancy opposition to, or concern for, the more than half-century use of carbaryl in Willapa Bay, even though year after year Ecology dutifully sent direct notice and invitation to comment on the annual spraying. (The Washington Chapter of the Nature Conservancy says they didn't have a formal position on the poisoning of the native shrimp.) Other environmental organizations did comment, including Washington Toxics Coalition, Defenders of Wildlife, and the Wise Use Movement.

"Agriculture took control in 1995," Marcial said as he recalled the sequence of events. "The local WSU extension guy, Kim Patten, had been working with the Willapa Refuge staff and declared the chemical glyphosate to be the cure. The 1993 environmental impact statement and emergency legislation paved the way for a massive chemical campaign. Permits were expedited, helicopters started spraying, and government departments flocked to the blizzard of grants. The Pacific County Noxious Weed Control Board was reduced to the role of watching and sending out threatening letters to tideland owners—and I got one. It said, 'You have an invasive species falling into the mandatory removal category so either give us permission to eradicate it for you, do it yourself, or the government will do it and send you the bill.'"

Not surprisingly, this didn't go over well with conservative Marcial as he lowered his voice as if shifting gears. "I've always had a problem with being threatened by my government."

So Marcial Hunter went to public meetings and listened. He talked with Agriculture staff about his biggest concern: what would the proposed chemical glyphosate do to the eelgrasses, duckgrass, and *marina*? As a hunter and scientist, Marcial knew that ducks and geese rely on eelgrass, and especially on duckgrass. "The Agriculture fellow seemed knowledgeable and asked me, 'Do your grasses trap a film of water when the tide goes out?' I said, 'Yes, they do.' The grasses were like soggy, poorly drained Astro-Turf after a rain. 'Well, the chemical will bleed into that film, it will be neutralized by the mud there, and it will not kill it,' he told me." And that was good enough for Marcial. When the state and federal agencies divided the bay up into management units, Marcial's intertidal property fell in the zone reserved for what he called the "Refuge Assault Team," a reference to the Willapa Refuge since it was just to the south of his property at the mouth of the Nemah River.

When the Refuge Assault Team called for permission to enter his property, he gave it.

They told him they probably wouldn't get to his property on the Nemah River flats until the following year. Being a nuclear engineer meant being a planner, and Marcial wanted a backup plan, so he studied to qualify for the state-issued Pesticide Applicator's License.

As it turned out, the Refuge Assault Team did make it to his place that first year. The helicopters had wide booms and sprayed glyphosate, sold under the brand name Rodeo. They flew so low, Marcial said, "I could almost read the name tag on the pilot's helmet." Marcial called his son in Louisiana, who had a buddy that worked at the Monsanto agricultural chemical plant there and asked him, "What in the heck is Rodeo?"

His son came back with, "Industrial strength Roundup."

Marcial read the Rodeo label.

It's a pesticide restricted for all aquatic use, allowed in Washington State only under a Special Local Need Registration. He learned that a strong surfactant would be added. Surfactants are chemicals used to help bind another chemical to its target, and can have greater toxicity than the chemical the surfactant is intended to help deliver. The pure glyphosate formulation, just mixed with water, would sit as a droplet on a waxy leaf surface, and the small area of contact provided little potential for uptake of the toxin into the foliage. Whereas, droplets containing a surfactant would spread in a thin layer over a waxy leaf surface and facilitate the glyphosate uptake by improving the toxin distribution on the leaf surface.

Surfactants can be toxic to humans, animals, and ecosystems, and formulations of some surfactants are kept secret by their manufacturer claiming the information to be proprietary. Since surfactants aren't required to be federally registered with the EPA, they do not normally undergo federal toxicity review. Marcial's research showed that R-11, the surfactant approved for use with glyphosate, could harm fish and invertebrates more than the chemical glyphosate did. In fact, of the surfactants studied at the time, R-11 was the one with the highest toxicity.

But as far as Marcial was concerned, if the Rodeo product label was followed, and it stuck to the plant and did not drip off for at least four hours before the tide came back in, it seemed a safe way to go.

"The good news was that it was true about the film of water. The duckgrass and *marina* survived. Or so it seemed. The bad news was that the glyphosate didn't kill the spartina either," Marcial said. It flat out didn't work.

In 1998, Agriculture proposed a higher broadcast application rate of glyphosate, but before EPA would approve this request, it required evidence that the proposed higher application rate of glyphosate would not result in residues in excess of the established tolerance for glyphosate in shellfish. So a study was done, largely funded by the public. The UW researchers conducted the study and found that, "Higher application rates specified on the 1998 Washington label for spartina control would ... not likely result in tissue concentrations of glyphosate that exceed the current tolerance for edible tissue."

INSTEAD, the UW researchers reported that their primary concerns with spartina in Willapa Bay were not related to chemical use or their non-target effects, but to the spread of spartina, loss of mudflats, and threat to the *duckgrass*. (Remember this when you get to the chapter about the future Shellfish Association permit to eradicate this same duckgrass.)

These tideflats, sans large meadows of spartina, were so essential to preserve that the state declared war on spartina to defend the tideflat functions—the same burrowing shrimp tideflats that the state and Shellfish Association had declared a wasteland: vacant, and barren, and so low in biological diversity that the ecosystem would be better served by eliminating the native shrimp and replacing them with non-native oysters.

Now, suddenly, the functions of these same tidelands were so valuable that an emergency was declared by the state legislature, which was prepared to unleash all manner of weapons to eradicate spartina, including large-scale herbicide use.

APPEALS

In 1997, 1998, and 1999, groups opposed to eradicating spartina by any method, and to large-scale spraying of pesticides in marine waters, filed permit appeals to stop the spraying of glyphosate on spartina in the estuarine environment, even after Senator Snyder's emergency legislation. After failing to persuade Governor Mike Lowry to **not** sign Senator Snyder's emergency legislation, the Ad Hoc Coalition of Willapa Bay appealed the Ecology-issued state pollution permit. Their group opposed the attempts to control spartina (especially with chemicals), which they believed was now part of the human-disturbed ecosystem in Willapa Bay and argued that the permit was inconsistent with state law.

However, no appeal succeeded in stopping the spraying.

From the state's perspective, the appeals consumed substantial Agriculture staff time, directly affecting the spartina eradication program statewide in 1999 and 2000, and with the wind and dry time restrictions, reducing the number of days applicators could spray glyphosate on spartina.

In the meantime, spartina was spreading. As Marcial recalled, "At the public meetings, they showed pictures of acres of dead spartina tops, but the tops of the spartina clumps on my tideflats that they sprayed with glyphosate did not look that dead. In most all areas, the massive roots were unfazed and it all came back."

The same precedent-setting federal court case in 2001, the

Headwaters ruling that determined pesticides applied to navigable waters were indeed pollution[8] and therefore required a Clean Water Act federal permit for carbaryl, now also applied to the spraying of glyphosate. This new requirement threw a monkey wrench into the glyphosate spraying, which was suspended in 2001 while Agriculture and Ecology worked on the new federal permit. All other mechanical forms of spartina control continued. State and local agencies coordinated with Ecology to develop a federal permit for statewide Aquatic Noxious Weed Control, with the hopes to resume glyphosate spraying in 2002.

And they did. The year 2002 was a year of mixed blessings. It was the year the Willapa Coalitions appealed the carbaryl permit that led to the Settlement Agreement to phase-out of carbaryl by 2012, but it was also the year that another pesticide, glyphosate, was granted a multi-year federal permit, to be sprayed into Willapa Bay, and to a lesser extent, Grays Harbor. As it turns out, native and non-native species were on par, both were the target of the growing pesticide industry.

After the state regained the use of glyphosate via the new federal permit, they started the process to use yet another chemical. By then, Marcial was following everything to do with spartina. "I started to pay close attention to the work of the local WSU extension agent, Kim Patten. He proposed a new chemical," Marcial said, "called imazapyr."

IMAZAPYR

It turns out that Monsanto's aquatic glyphosate recipe alone couldn't "save" Willapa Bay from spartina after all. WSU's Kim Patten had

---

[8] In November 2006, EPA issued a new rule concerning the use of pesticides in or around waters of the United States. The rule states that any pesticide meant for use in or near water, applied in accordance with the FIFRA label, is not a pollutant under the CWA. Therefore, such applications are not subject to NPDES permitting.

been testing this new chemical, imazapyr, in Willapa Bay for about a decade, but it wasn't yet approved for aquatic use. To expedite imazapyr's approval for aquatic use, EPA concurrently evaluated imazapyr for aquatic use while Agriculture prepared the environmental review for that chemical.

In a Letter to the Editor of the local Willapa paper, *The Chinook Observer*, Miranda Wecker of Naselle, who worked for the Willapa Alliance, UW, and who was then appointed by the Governor to the DFW Commission, helped shed light on how imazapyr was approved for use in Washington marine waters by the EPA:

> Patty Murray has earned my support and deserves re-election … I have had first-hand experiences that have convinced me who Patty Murray is. Over the past 20 years, I spent a good chunk of my life working to reverse the spread of invasive spartina in Willapa Bay. In the early 2000s, things looked bleak. We needed help. Patty Murray took a personal interest in our little corner of the state.
>
> Yes, she helped us with federal funding. There is no doubt that, without those earmarks, our bay would be overrun with that invasive weed. But Patty did more than that.
>
> During one of her visits to our area, a community group discussed our problems. We told her that the EPA process for approving new herbicides was terribly backlogged and would not even begin to look at imazapyr, the herbicide we hoped to use, for about five to seven years. That delay was sure to cost us thousands of acres of bay lost to spartina.
>
> Patty heard us: she personally visited EPA headquarters in Washington to explain the urgency. EPA officials told me later that no senator had ever done that. EPA moved up their review. The evidence supporting imazapyr's safety and effectiveness was overwhelming. EPA approved the use of imazapyr within the next year and the results in our bay are visible: Spartina has almost been eliminated and the mudflats

are returning to their productivity. If you have ever met her, you know that Patty is a decent and warm person. She has little of the ego that is common to powerful people. That is because she is in politics for the right reasons: to serve our country and people. It's time to make sure she gets another term as the most effective senator Washington has ever had.

EPA approved imazapyr, manufactured by BASF, for aquatic use in 2003, and the pesticide was immediately put to the test at a very large scale in Willapa Bay.

Ecology added imazapyr to the standing five-year federal permit for glyphosate, a decision that Marcial characterizes as "a sleight of hand," because imazapyr contains a powerful acetolactate synthase inhibitor (ALS inhibitor) and glyphosate does not. ALS inhibitors are non-selective, disrupt plant protein synthesis, and interfere with cell growth. Like glyphosate, imazapyr is water-soluble and could move into parts of the landscape where it wasn't sprayed.

All along Marcial was deeply concerned for the bay's eelgrasses because of the vital role they play in the ecosystem, and was willing to go along with glyphosate because it wouldn't necessarily kill eelgrass. But imazapyr was different. "A chemical that kills eelgrass doesn't belong in the same permit as one that does not," Marcial said, with more than a hint of disbelief.

KEEP OFF MY LAND

"The elixir recommended by Agriculture for my pesticide applicators license was called a 'tank mix.' It contained the maximum allowable strength of glyphosate; the maximum allowable strength of imazapyr in a product labeled HABITAT; and the maximum allowable strength of the surfactant R-11, the fish and invertebrate killer," Marcial recalled. "When I got my letter from the Pacific County Noxious

Weed Control Board, with the same threats, I noticed there was a new section where I would have to agree to never hold the Weed Board liable for problems. That, I would not sign. I called the Willapa Refuge staff and told them to keep out," Marcial said.

Next, he went out and flagged the property line of his tidelands. He called his Agriculture contact and told him that he was worried about the two chemicals in combination, because from what he had learned, the glyphosate would kill the spartina foliage, shutting off the biology of the plant before the new chemical—imazapyr—could kill the root. Marcial asked if this imazapyr would kill his eelgrass. "The answer was, if it gets in that film of water that adheres to the eelgrass, then, yes it would!" The combination of the surfactant R-11, lethal to fish and invertebrates, and now imazapyr, lethal to eelgrass, was a combination that almost pushed Marcial over the edge.

Imazapyr deserved a hard look considering that thousands of gallons of imazapyr-based solution were being considered for massive application to Willapa Bay and other Washington marine waters. The EPA assessments showed that imazapyr had low toxicity levels when it came to animals and humans. A long look at EPA documents, however, reveals that regulators used data from tests on freshwater species to assume that imazapyr would be just as "safe" in saltwater areas like Willapa Bay. In other words, no testing was done on the long-term effects imazapyr could have on saltwater fish and the tiny organisms at the base of the marine food chain. In addition, EPA did not evaluate the toxicity of imazapyr when mixed with the other chemicals like glyphosate or surfactants in formulas used in the field. The EPA told *Truthout*, an online news website focused on systemic injustices, that the assessment was sound and no data gaps existed.

Agriculture's own risk assessment for the spartina project admits that little was known about imazapyr's long-term effects on organisms that make up the foundation of the food chain, such as invertebrates and phytoplankton, and there is no data on how long imazapyr stays active within dead spartina. The appendix to the risk assessment indicates imazapyr persists in soils for up to six months. The report concludes that the toxicity of imazapyr is so low that these data gaps are of no concern.

Truthout interviewed Cynthia Lopez, who, years later, said that there were too many holes in this story. Lopez is a former Washington State Health Department official who chaired an interagency committee on pesticides and public health until the program was slashed in 2009 due to state budget cuts. She reviewed the EPA's assessment of imazapyr and concluded that more testing should have been done before allowing massive sprays in Willapa Bay. "Imazapyr is dangerous in that the effects are unknown," Lopez said in the *Truthout* interview. "There really hasn't been any long-term investigation into the safety of this product." Lopez pointed out that, when imazapyr was first registered, it was restricted from use near water, and very little new data was used to justify its use in aquatic areas. "We have this ongoing experiment going on ... is this the way to do it?" she asked.

So imazapyr and glyphosate were not tested on all species of wildlife that used the estuaries, the mixture of the two together was never tested for toxicity or other synergistic effects, they both persisted in the soils, and if and how they broke down or accumulated in aquatic ecosystems was, and is still, unknown.

Marcial was concerned. "Just as I anticipated after thoroughly researching these chemicals, when they combined glyphosate with the imazapyr, they couldn't tell if the roots had been killed because the glyphosate killed only the tops, which masked if the root had been killed yet by the imazapyr." Then Marcial emphasized, "It was the WRONG chemical cocktail and I refused to use it for that reason."

"For another four years, I schlepped around in the mud wearing a backpack sprayer, but this time it was just imazapyr and whatever surfactant they recommended. I kept that stuff off the mud and off my eelgrass. I used no more glyphosate in the bay, but others did in a cocktail that included both imazapyr and glyphosate. My results were better than theirs were. I painfully watched them repeatedly spray some areas before the spartina was gone," Marcial said. "While I successfully killed the spartina on my land with imazapyr alone, and saved my eelgrass, all around me it felt like D-Day roared. There was sloppiness to put it mildly. These guys sprayed fifteen minutes in front of the incoming tide, which was unbelievable, from both helicopters and airboats.

From 1997 to 2011, Agriculture lead the effort to mow and spray spartina in Willapa Bay on 28,000 acres, some of which were sprayed two or more times in a year with glyphosate, imazapyr, and the surfactant R-11.
(Source: Agriculture)

"Over those years I watched the same areas get sprayed five times whereas it should have been only once or twice with just imazapyr. And I never saw the oystering slow down, even though the imazapyr label said not to spray on food crops, and if you did, to not sell a crop for 180 days. An alternate way to sell was to sample the crop and verify that minimal contamination measured in parts per billion was met."

With skepticism Marcial stated, "Surely they did those measurements?" Then, as if to answer his own question, he said, "But I suspect those folks in Seattle were eating imazapyr and trusting the government."[9]

Marcial was allowed to spray under an Agriculture permit for glyphosate and imazapyr only with supervision. Several years into Marcial's five-year spartina eradication program on his privately owned tidelands, his pesticide applicator license manager visited his property. Marcial said the Agriculture staff was shocked. "He said, 'You got rid of all your spartina! How did you do that?' I told him 'I followed the directions. And look at my duckgrass!'" Marcial's tideland property was an island of green in a vast brown mudflat. His eelgrass survived, but not the eelgrass in other parts of the bay.

"I knew there was an agency spartina meeting coming up at the Willapa Wildlife Refuge," Marcial recalled. "I told my Agriculture staff contact to tell everyone there that I never want to see that stupid marsh buggy around here again, or they'll be in trouble." Marcial reported to the Agriculture staff person that the marsh buggy that the agencies used to spray the tank mix from the ground left three brown stripes and four green stripes, evident the following year. Marcial showed him some of this ground. The reason for the green stripes, which should have been brown, was that the marsh buggy's wide tracks ran right over what had just been sprayed, disrupting the toxic chemical's contact with the plant.

In addition, Marcial told him that in this instance, no spray came out of the far end of the nozzles on both sides. Marcial said that he had reported the clogged nozzle issue to the Willapa Wildlife Refuge Manager earlier, but was told this was not possible because the rules require the gear to be checked each day.

---

[9] Agriculture responded to a records request that they have no record of monitoring oysters for uptake of imazapyr.

This was a turning point for Marcial, who isn't inclined to make rash decisions. "At that point, I just decided no more Mr. Nice Guy. Apparently, they got my message. I never saw the marsh buggy again," Marcial said. As a "three strikes and you're out" kind of a guy, Marcial's opinion of public employees and political appointees was cemented. "I was forming an opinion about the reliability of the WSU and UW staff in these matters. It seemed clear to me that the years of their chemical trials—that they touted to get these poisons approved—were ineffective. They declared glyphosate effective and it was not. Imazapyr alone worked, but they unnecessarily added glyphosate to the tank mix." Marcial believed that imazapyr with glyphosate unnecessarily prolonged the use of toxins in the estuaries. WSU's Kim Patten would go on to earn worldwide acclaim by discovering that he could kill off spartina with imazapyr, an herbicide previously used along railroad tracks.

BIRTH OF AN ENVIRONMENTAL ACTIVIST

"From my perspective, once the glyphosate and R-11 permit was issued, they felt free to tinker with it without public involvement. It seemed to me that Ecology was winking while DFW was seeing no evil to wildlife," Marcial said.

Five very different people: Larry Warnberg, organic oysterman; Ernie Summers, Washington Dungeness Crab Association President; Herb Whitish, Shoalwater Tribal Chairman; Fritzi Cohen, innkeeper and oyster grower; and now Marcial Hunter, each came to view all state action in the area with suspicion and cynicism. And the five of them became outspoken environmental activists against the use of pesticides in these marine waters.

Each cared enough to educate themselves on the management of Willapa Bay and Grays Harbor. Larry, seeking a career in what he thought was a sustainable industry; Ernie, as a lifelong resident and harvester; Herb, raising alarm about the tribe's pregnancy crises; Fritzi, well, only as Fritzi can be; and Marcial, as a tideland owner and avid sportsman. But without a powerful resource industry and lobby behind them, they were powerless against the state that appeared to favor special interest groups over the health of the ecosystem and the animals.

Thirty million dollars later, the spartina eradication program was deemed a success.

On Willapa Bay, there are so few spartina clumps that people jokingly say they have named them.

But it's not over for Marcial, who thought he would be relaxing in his sunset years, hunting migratory ducks and geese. Instead, he finds himself trying to fill the void left by Ecology: unsuccessfully (so far) trying to protect Willapa Bay duckgrasses from the Shellfish Association's plan to eradicate it along with *marina* (the same eelgrasses that everyone was trying to protect from spartina). He's also trying to stop state approval of a carbaryl replacement chemical, the neonicotinoid imidacloprid—under consideration by Ecology as of February 2018.

This narrative doesn't capture the entire spartina story, but the story of the shellfish companies' ongoing use of pesticides must continue.

Before it's too late.

CHAPTER 15: SCIENCE?

"When we signed the Settlement Agreement in 2003 with the Shellfish Association, we made sure that future shrimp control did not include more chemicals, after the generous ten years we gave them to phase out carbaryl. We didn't anticipate that state and federal agencies would step in with the public wallet and do it for the nozzleheads," Larry said, expressing the betrayal he felt.

Since the Settlement Agreement tied the hands of the Shellfish Association from developing new chemicals, they got the government to do it for them, opening up a new flow of state and federal funds in the war on the shrimp, including a carbaryl replacement pesticide.

Tao Orion wrote in *Beyond the War on Invasive Species*, that there are three disturbing trends in the restoration industry (associated with invasive species). She writes that these are: close cooperation between federal and state policy makers and pesticide manufacturers (e.g., Monsanto sitting side-by-side with Senator Snyder, guiding state policy); another is the relationship between trusted nonprofit conservation organizations and these same industries; and the third is the relationship between publicly funded land grant universities and the pesticide manufacturers.

CONSERVATION ORGANIZATION CAPTURE

Orion wrote, "Rachel Carson dedicated a chapter of *Silent Spring* to denounce the use of organophosphate herbicides (which includes glyphosate) that the Nature Conservancy now recommends. In an ironic twist of fate, Carson, who died an untimely death from breast cancer, dedicated one third of her estate to the Nature Conservancy."

More recently, the Nature Conservancy's website names Monsanto, the manufacturer of DDT, Agent Orange, and other agriculture chemicals whose use Carson opposed, as a corporate partner. Other corporate partners include Dow Chemical, Cargill, Pepsi, Coca-Cola, and the multinational mining company Rio Tinto. Companies like Coca-Cola and Cargill that derive profit from converting biodiverse prairies and rainforest into commodity crops like corn for corn syrup and soy for animal feed, make strange bedfellows for an organization that is revered for protecting those same ecosystems from development "for nature's sake."

The Washington Chapter of the Nature Conservancy has been an advocate for pesticide use in Willapa Bay: glyphosate and imazapyr to kill spartina, and imazamox to kill ecologically significant eelgrasses relied upon by numerous species including migratory ducks and geese (covered in the last chapter), and there is no record of Nature Conservancy opposition to use of carbaryl to kill native species to benefit non-native shellfish, even though the state sent notice to their Seattle office of the annual spraying.

Robin Stanton, Media Manager for the Nature Conservancy, says they did not have a formal position on the spraying of the native shrimp.

UNIVERSITY CAPTURE

The Washington State Legislature, DFW, Agriculture, Ecology,

USDA, and US National Oceanic & Atmospheric Administration—all subsidize the shellfish industry, including research on pesticides.

But Washington State University's role takes the cake.

In the nineteenth century, the U.S. granted 17.5 million acres of federally owned land to states for the establishment of publicly funded land grant universities. This land, and the universities now sited on it, form the backbone of agriculture research in the U.S. and provide benefits to students and farmers from their extension offices, publications, and educational offerings. Every state has at least one land grant college or university. These universities are also home to agricultural experiment stations and cooperative extension offices, many of which have developed commercially available varieties of food and ornamental crops.

These universities were established for the public good and are still funded by public tax dollars. They are, in principle, beholden to the public trust. These days, many of the land grant institutions receive large endowments from private sector companies, especially large agribusiness corporations like Monsanto, Cargill, Syngenta, and DuPont.

A 2012 report from Food and Water Watch found that nearly 25 percent of funding for agriculture research at public institutions comes from private companies. These companies also fund the development of new campus infrastructure, provide money for endowed professorships, and enlist industry representatives to sit on research committees that decide on departmental funding and project proposals. At New Mexico State University for instance, Dow Chemical, Monsanto, and BASF provided herbicide and several small grants to help with its efforts to educate landowners about invasive plant species and how to manage them.

The consumer group, U.S. Right to Know, recently filed a lawsuit against the University of California, Davis for failing to release public records on genetically engineered organisms and pesticides.

"We are conducting a wide-ranging investigation into the collaboration between the food and agrichemical industries, their front groups, and several U.S. universities," said Gary Ruskin, co-director of U.S. Right to Know. "So far, documents obtained from other universities have shown secretive funding arrangements and covert efforts to use taxpayer-funded university resources to promote the products of various corporations. The public has a right to know what is going on behind the scenes."

Most aspiring college-bound students probably don't think of WSU as a pesticide advocate, yet WSU leads in its support of pesticide use in Willapa Bay and Grays Harbor, areas described by the shellfish companies on their websites and elsewhere as "pristine." WSU provides both financial and staff support for the use of pesticides in these bays.

On a related note, in 2017, the Washington State Executive Ethics Board (ethics board) conducted a six-month investigation into WSU's Kim Patten. The ethics board found that Patten—who had conducted a significant portion of the science for almost every pesticide in Willapa Bay for decades—had a conflict of interest.

Ethics board Chair John Ladenburg Sr. said in an interview with the *Seattle Times* that Patten used his government computer, an official email account, and his position as a government scientist to promote his own private interests.

According to the investigation, Patten submitted multiple comments to the Washington State Noxious Weed Control Board both as a scientist and as the owner of a private clam bed. The Weed Control Board was considering proposals for the use of the pesticide imazamox to kill duckgrass (critical food for migratory waterfowl) because the shellfish growers said it interfered with their non-native shellfish beds *(discussed in detail in the final chapter).*

Patten supported the use of the pesticide, but also stood to benefit if it was approved, Ladenburg said. "He has a conflict of interest in the whole process of influencing the Weed Control Board. If it goes his way, his land is more valuable, so that raises the question of whether he is being a disinterested scientist ... or is he trying to manipulate the government to do things that benefit him?"

As reported by the *Seattle Times*, Patten characterized the infraction as a clerical error and said he agreed to the fine to avoid a costly and time-consuming legal battle. However, the ethics board was particularly concerned that Patten's conflicts cropped up several times, and could undermine confidence in his research.

"You can see how this looks to the public," Ladenburg said. "Now people are going to question all his research because he had a personal interest."

But Patten says his only lapse was failing to remove his WSU signature page from comments sent to the Weed Control Board via a Gmail account that he uses for both work and personal messages because WSU's email system doesn't work well on the coast. Patten also said the ethics case should not call his research into question.[10]

And Ecology agreed.

Ecology told the *Seattle Times* that the ethical violations "were not related to the quality of (Patten's) research," and that his work remains part of the record. "My research and study has spanned almost thirty years, with a singular focus on preserving the ecology and economy of Willapa Bay," Patten wrote in an email cited by the *Seattle Times*. "My life's work has been devoted to this effort, and it is

---

[10] According to Patten's resume, he has received "Gifts and Awards" from these chemical manufacturers, one of which was labeled, "Unrestricted Gift": DuPont, Certis, Bayer CropScience, Dow Chemical & Dow AgroSciences, United Phosphorous, Chemtura Corporation, Sepro, BASF, Makhteshim-Again, and VALENT, totaling $104,300.

vital that we move forward in focusing on scientific study." WSU did not take any action against him, he added.

Indeed, WSU's Michael J. Gaffrey wrote a letter to Patten, "I want you to know that you are a highly valued faculty member at an institution at which accountability and adherence to Washington State Law are paramount. My expectation is that you will continue to act in accordance to that status." When contacted for this book, WSU said they would not comment on a personnel matter.

But the investigation revealed more. Patten had a financial relationship with the Sheldons of Northern Oyster Company.

In 2013, Patten negotiated a private clam lease with Brian Sheldon using his WSU email, and in that same email exchange, Sheldon requested that Patten attend an upcoming Ecology meeting regarding the proposed use of imazamox to poison Willapa Bay eelgrass, for which Patten conducted some of the studies as a WSU employee. Brian Sheldon wrote to Patten, "Also, Nate at DOE has asked for a meet on December 13 down here. He said they want to discuss some changes they want to make to the draft NPDES permit. If you're available, I may be asking you to attend."

Not only do the Sheldons own a large shellfish operation on Willapa Bay, father and son serve on the state's Oyster Reserves Advisory Committee (composed of shellfish representatives), which recommends state funding—including funding of Patten's pesticide research—for the shellfish industry. In addition, Brian Sheldon is a Shellfish Association Board member, and a shellfish pesticide applicant.

WSU FIELD STATION ... CONTAMINATED

Perhaps ironically symbolic, the WSU outpost in Long Beach is contaminated with pesticides and a metal (arsenic) from WSU's pesticide research in support of the cranberry industry, and from on-site disposal of many of those same pesticides.

Not only was the soil and groundwater contaminated on their site, groundwater carried the contamination to their neighbor's residential wells.

In 1998, the Department of Health stepped in to assure the people whose wells were contaminated that it was okay to drink the contaminated water, and that there should be no adverse affects from drinking it. After WSU prepared a site assessment, Ecology determined that the preferred remedial alternative for the site was long-term groundwater monitoring.

A decade later, Ecology was back with a Notice of Violation—addressed to Kim Patten—for the Long Beach field station concerning stains on the ground near an ammonia-rinsing area that Ecology staff believed was from an unspecified hazardous material, and suggested that WSU inventory the pesticides onsite, some of which appeared to be past their pull date.

WSU SCIENTISTS TO THE RESCUE

WSU staff diligently pursued more pesticides to use on the native shrimp. As early as 1996, WSU's Alan Schreiber led chemical trials to find a replacement for carbaryl. He injected several chemicals into the sediments, including imidacloprid, abamectin, diflubenzuron, and fenoxycarb. But the pesticide imidacloprid is intended for use only on land. The label makes this explicit: "This product is highly toxic to aquatic invertebrates. Do not apply directly to water, or to areas where surface water is present, or to intertidal areas below the mean high water mark."

Schreiber put imidacloprid into Willapa Bay while wearing his WSU hat—and relied on public funds from the Washington Commission on Pesticide Registration (where he also worked as Administrator) to do so. Mysteriously, carbaryl was detected throughout the test area for the 1996 trials even though it was not included in the study. The researchers concluded that the carbaryl was of unknown origin. The presence of the "mystery" carbaryl bogied the effectiveness of the trial chemicals. The studies were not valid for that reason.

But was this really a mystery? Could it be that carbaryl, found in Willapa Bay outside the permit window, was being sprayed illegally (which was consistent with reports by Larry and others), or that carbaryl was still in the system from the last spray season? Or perhaps both? Ecology had record of at least three water quality studies done in 1988, 1996, and 1997 that found carbaryl at levels unsafe for marine life BEFORE permitted spraying had started, yet there is no record of Ecology investigating the source of this contamination or any penalties imposed for illegal spraying.

In 2004, a mere year into the Settlement Agreement to phase out chemicals completely, WSU staff ratcheted up their experiments by injecting more than twenty pesticides into the tidelands in a race to find a replacement pesticide for the increasingly politically toxic carbaryl. Sulfur[11], Poncho, Pyganic, Veratran, Thiosol, Ecotrol, Ecozone, Mustang, Deltaguard, Esteem, Capture, Ecozone, Carbaryl, and Imidacloprid, were injected.

The work plan sings with precision: "Application will be by Taylor Shellfish's semi-amphibious heavy vehicle (e.g., the Rolligon™) modified to not only inject material subsurface, but also to disrupt shrimp burrows causing both direct mortality and dislodging of the shrimp to the surface for exposure to birds and other predators. The Rolligon is modified to pull a set of six shanks spaced one foot apart. The shanks can also inject liquid subsurface at high water pressures and volumes. The shanks are modified to

---

[11] The Sulfur label also says, "Do Not Apply to Water…" yet Ecology and Agriculture both approved these experiments with no evidence of public comment or in-depth environmental analyses.

vibrate, thus further disrupting shrimp burrows. Shanking, injection, and vibration can be executed independently or in combination."

Their quest for a new pesticide turned the Settlement Agreement on its head.

Here's another example of how public funds flow. The Shellfish Association was concerned that lower overall toxicity of imidacloprid, compared to carbaryl, would not be as effective for killing shrimp. A study was needed. So the state funded the "Fate, Non-target Impacts and Commercial Feasibility of Estuarine Use of Imidacloprid" study in 2012 to 2013. The legislature gave the funds to WSU, which engaged a committee made up of shellfish companies and WSU staff to dispense the funds to WSU's Kim Patten, UW staff, and the Pacific Shellfish Institute (research arm of the shellfish industry). The USDA was a project cooperator.

Patten helped analyze all the various chemicals in order to come up with a proposed replacement chemical for carbaryl, one that they started to characterize as environmentally benign, a gentle poison, one with a light touch, less toxic than carbaryl. Their choice was imidacloprid, the increasingly notorious neonicinitoid responsible in part for the worldwide honeybee colony collapse.

On an almost parallel track, Patten started to develop a pesticide program to rid the shellfish companies of the pesky eelgrasses, honing in on an herbicide called imazamox. Remember, this was the same eelgrass they previously claimed benefitted from the poisoning of the shrimp and spartina. *(Note: The history of imidacloprid is told first, followed by the history of imazamox, although their time-lines overlap.)* The backstory for how WSU staff aided the shellfish industry to get EPA approval to use a chemical never intended for use in the water can be found in Bill Donahue's 2015 story in *Bloomberg Business News*, "Washington State Turns to Neurotoxins to Save Its Oysters."

Imidacloprid, created in 1986 and first registered in 1994 by

CHAPTER 15: SCIENCE?

Bayer (a $4 billion German chemical and pharmaceutical firm) is no longer proprietary—it went off patent in 2005. But David Fischer, an ecotoxicologist with Bayer CropScience, speaks of imidacloprid with parental pride. "It's far safer than chemicals like carbaryl," he said. "You can handle it without any health risks, and you need only about one-tenth as much of it. And it's precise, too. It can target certain receptors in invertebrates that you don't have in higher animals like birds and humans."

Research on imidacloprid paints a much darker picture. In one 2012 study published in *Science,* British researchers found that bees fed sugar water spiked with neonicotinoids (neonics) were less able than control bees to produce queens in their hives. They didn't gather enough food.

In another study published in the same issue of *Science,* French researchers found that bees fed neonics had difficulty getting back to the hive from a half-mile away. Neonic defenders have maintained that bees could learn to avoid treated plants, but in a study published in *Nature,* Geraldine Wright, a British researcher, found that this was not so. Wright sequestered honeybees in boxes and gave them a choice between plain nectar and nectar laced with neonics. The bees favored the poisoned nectar.

Imidacloprid is largely banned in Europe, and facing a proposed ban in Canada due to its severe impacts on—aquatic species.

A 2014 Dutch study, published in *Nature,* found that the population of insect-eating birds declines rapidly—3.5 percent a year—in areas with high concentrations of neonics on the surface of the water. The birds died, the authors believe, because they were eating poisoned bugs.

Another 2014 study, published in the *Japanese Journal of Clinical Ecology,* found that when patients in Gunma prefecture consumed imidacloprid-treated food, they were inordinately inclined to record abnormal cardiograms and to complain of chest and muscle pains.

Patten relentlessly pursued EPA registration of imidacloprid. The state and industry were fully behind him.

In 2008, EPA determined that imidacloprid was highly toxic to aquatic organisms, highly soluble in water, resistant to degradation in soil and water, and able to translocate in plants.

For example, in the same 2008 EPA report, staff cited a study that found imidacloprid residues in blossoms and leaves of ornamental plants for as long as *540 days* after treatment of surrounding soil *(emphasis added)*.

In that same 2008 EPA report, staff said they expected the mere use of imidacloprid outdoors to affect endangered species. They went on to say exposure to imidacloprid could cause direct acute and chronic risk to endangered and non-target aquatic invertebrates.

But then, five years later, EPA said that spraying imidacloprid into Willapa Bay and Grays Harbor was safe enough for its approval.

Kim Patten was jubilant. "That was a miracle," he said of the EPA's decision in an interview with Bill Donahue. He never thought it would happen.

CHAPTER 16: THOSE PESKY PESTS

W hen the EPA gave a thumbs-up in June 2013 to spray imidacloprid directly into estuarine waters to kill aquatic invertebrates, it left the final decision on imidacloprid use to Ecology. The Department of Ecology. The same state agency recently sued for not doing its job to protect the Puget Sound environment, jeopardizing millions of dollars in federal grant funding. The state agency Marcial refers to as "The Agency-With-The-Wrong-Name."

Ecology. "They're the weakest agency on earth," Andrea Rodgers said in an interview with *Crosscut*. Rodgers is an attorney with the Western Environmental Law Center, a Eugene-based firm that works pro bono throughout the region. "And they have good reason to be scared of the people they're supposed to regulate. Every time they use their regulatory authority, agriculture runs to the legislature and gets their budget cut, and their authority cut."

When 2013 rolled around, the Shellfish Association didn't have imidacloprid approved yet, so they asked Ecology for another carbaryl year. What would Ecology say to another year of carbaryl … in violation of Larry and Fritzi's hard-won Settlement Agreement that had already generously granted ten years, at the end of which the half-century of spraying was to end by December 2012? Ecology, the agency that seldom if ever said "No" to the shellfish industry? The agency that acquiesced to carbaryl year after year in the face of massive casualties and industry claims that this was good for the environment?

Was Ecology going to protect the environment and represent the public that depends on healthy and inter-connected ecosystems for human survival?

Ecology gave a thumbs-up with no public comment or opportunity for appeal. Continued use of carbaryl, even with Ecology's approval, violated the Willapa Coalition's hard-won Settlement Agreement in which the Shellfish Association promised, once and for all, the last and final year of carbaryl use would be 2012.

Disgusted, Larry Warnberg said, "Ecology was not party to the Agreement; let the Growers spray."

In the Regulatory Capture model, those with money control the public agencies. Those without money, don't. "Our Settlement Agreement required arbitration for conflicts, which would have cost us unknown bucks, so we let it go."

Although Larry and Fritzi opposed the carbaryl spraying in 2013, they didn't have the money or energy to fight once more.

After Marcial Hunter's brush with the state and shellfish companies over the eradication of spartina, he was now paying close attention to chemical use on Willapa Bay. "The oyster guys didn't have all their approvals for imidacloprid in time for the 2013 or 2014 spraying," Marcial explained. "They got Ecology to allow another carbaryl year in 2013, and in 2014, they got Ecology to use the same tactic for imidacloprid that they did when they added imazapyr to the glyphosate permit. Imidacloprid was an unpermitted chemical. So they called it a 'test' under the still-active carbaryl permit, and sprayed hundreds of acres in 2014. Ecology left the carbaryl permit conveniently active, even after EPA banned its use in or near water.

Spraying an unpermitted chemical in the bay under a permit for a banned chemical; that was quite the trick," Marcial said, but not with admiration.[12]

Can the Shellfish Association be expected to behave in ways that do not produce rewards? The industry has been rewarded by planning and strategic investments. They received their public land for next to nothing. They have one of the oldest industry associations in the state lobbying their interests, and two publicly funded shellfish labs. After an amendment to a state statute in 2001, they now have influence over money generated from the Oyster Reserves, the majority of which is spent on shellfish "pest" research of which a good portion is awarded to WSU, UW, and to the industry's Pacific Shellfish Institute to conduct pesticide studies.

When DNR staff attempted to collect a market rent on the few remaining tidelands owned by the public, the attempt was reportedly squashed by elected officials. The Pacific Coast Shellfish Growers Association strategically spun off a non-profit private research arm in 1994—the Pacific Shellfish Institute—to take receipt of public funds to conduct custom research to benefit the shellfish industry. Commercial aquaculture is exempt from DFW permits, evidently at DFW's discretion (an exemption others don't enjoy), and they appear to exercise inordinate influence over Ecology. Over the years, they molded the state Shoreline Management Act, fisheries laws, water quality standards, and various other statutes and codes to benefit aquatic farming.

All in all, their war on the burrowing shrimp was a success. Without any study of the native shrimp populations, they were able to unleash an annual spraying regimen of the indiscriminate

---

[12] The EPA allowed large-scale application of imidacloprid into Willapa Bay from 2008-2010, prior to its registration for aquatic use in 2014... a use previously banned because it is highly toxic to aquatic invertebrates.

neurotoxic carbaryl, and use it from 1963 to 2013, alleged illegal use notwithstanding. The one year they didn't spray was 2001, but *only* out of fear of a lawsuit, accompanied with complaints for how much money they would lose. Now, their plans for a replacement pesticide, imidacloprid, were falling into place, apparently with little to no resistance from state agencies or the EPA.

PESKY PESTS

Perhaps emboldened with their success for carbaryl use, and evident lack of enforcement for complaints when used illegally, it was time for a plan to deal with all the other native species they claimed interfered with their shellfish-growing operations. They devised a plan that could legally deter, suppress, or destroy mostly native species that were bothersome to industrial-scale mono-crop shellfish operations in the coastal and interior water ways, not just the besieged native shrimp or the eelgrass and duckgrass that are now faced with an annual toxic dose of imazamox, whose story is about to be told.

It turns out, approval to switch to imidacloprid to kill the native shrimp, and approval to douse imazamox into Willapa Bay to kill the eelgrasses, were just one part of a much larger industry strategic plan—a plan that laid out an assault on any plant or animal that got in the way of the shellfish industry.

This plan wasn't leaked by a disgruntled or concerned employee; it wasn't prepared in the proverbial smoke-filled backrooms of the Shellfish Association or the Pacific Coast Shellfish Growers Association. It was paid for *by the public* and prepared by people affiliated with public agencies. And the shellfish industry.

The Pest Plan for controlling native species that the shellfish industry considers "pests" was funded and prepared by the USDA and Oregon State University. The Work Group members included the

Shellfish Association, the Pacific Coast Shellfish Growers Association, various shellfish companies, DFW, WSU's Kim Patten, Squaxin Island Tribe (which has a shellfish operation), the USDA, and Agriculture.

Staff for this project tried to keep Puget Sound tideland owner Laura Hendricks from attending one of its meetings in Long Beach, and told her that there was no room. She went anyway.

Laura was a Sierra Club volunteer and chair of its Shorelines and Aquaculture sub-committee. It turns out that the auditorium was big enough for hundreds of people and there were only about forty there. Curious as to how Oregon State University ended up leading the effort, a grower at the meeting told Laura that Taylor Shellfish asked them to. She kept a low profile and sat in the back.

First drafted in 2010, the Pest Plan goal was to maximize production of mono-crop-farmed shellfish: oysters, clams, geoducks (a large clam) and mussels. The Pest Plan spelled out chemical, biological, and operational controls for what they deemed as pests. It identified regulatory hurdles that had to be taken down for the industry to achieve its pest elimination, or management goals.

The Major Pests section of the Pest Plan identifies these animals as pests, followed by a proposed control:

1) Native polychaete worms and non-native bamboo worms: poison. (This includes the polychaete worms in Willapa Bay that share space with the shrimp, and whose burrows are hard to tell apart from the shrimp burrow.)

2) Native barnacles: remove by hand, which the plan noted adds substantial labor costs to the growers.

3) Native burrowing shrimp: poison.

4) Native cockles: remove by hand, which the plan noted adds substantial labor costs to the growers. This section recommends developing a market for cockles to convert them to cash.

5) Native Dungeness, Rock, Graceful Crabs, and non-native Green crab: hand removal and relocation of crabs.

6) Flatworms: dip in fresh water to kill.

7) Native horse clams: remove during geoduck harvest. The plan recommends finding a way to convert horse clams to cash.

8) Native moon snail: remove the snails and their egg cases, explore ways to develop a market for the snail and convert to cash.

9) Industry-introduced, non-native oyster drills: remove the drill (a type of snail) by hand along with its egg case, and rototill the tidelands to kill.

10) Native sand dollars: pick by hand and throw onto upper inter-tidal in bed preparation, then deploy barrier netting to exclude the sand dollars from their habitat.

11) Native starfish: remove by hand and deploy barrier netting on tidelands to exclude starfish from their habitat.

Yet *actual* shellfish farmer practices reveal a starker and even darker reality.

The reality is, native sand dollars are cleared from the tidelands and thrown up onto higher ground to die.

"Sand dollar beds are uncommon and may be declining in Puget Sound, but they are a key ecological species controlling local communities, may serve as refuges for young Dungeness crabs, and do not return to beaches once lost," wrote three ecologists concerned with geoduck farming impacts to sand dollars.

The reality is, native starfish are dismembered or poisoned.

The reality is, crabs are dismembered, poisoned, and left to die.

Native Sand dollars removed and thrown higher up on beach to die

In Puget Sound and Hood Canal, shellfish growers dismember the crabs to eliminate them from feeding on their non-native clams and oysters. "That's not all," said a former large shellfish company employee in an interview for this book when he returned from his shop carrying a container of carbaryl. "The owners would have employees soak salmon carcasses in carbaryl, then place them on the oyster beds. The toxic bait would kill the crab, along with other animals attracted by the poisoned bait."

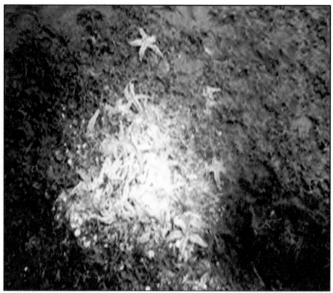

Native Starfish gathered and killed with quick lime

The Pest Plan says that the native algae, sea lettuce and eelgrasses, are major problems. It reduces these ecologically vital aquatic plants to ... weeds. The recommended control of algae and eelgrasses is to sweep them from the nets placed over the geoduck and clam farms, or to harrow the tidelands to rid them of these native plants.

As for the ecologically vital non-native duckgrass, so important to save from spartina, the Pest Plan calls for its mechanical removal, and notes that, at that moment, no pesticides are registered to use against duckgrass. Not yet.

The industry complains that BOTH species of eelgrass interfere with crop yields, seed larvae recruitment, and growth. The draft of the Pest Plan handed out at the March 2010 meeting in Long Beach acknowledged that the native Willapa Bay eelgrass, *Zostera marina*, was "mowed" by dragging cutting blades over the beds, with a typed question in parentheses asking "(Ok to leave in?)"

Geoduck harvesting, which impacts eelgrass beds.
Below is a list of 55 species that rely on eelgrass as their habitat:

1. zooplankton
2. larval crab
3. salmon
4. herring
5. epiphytic macroalgae
6. epiphytic microalgae, hydozoa, and bryozoa
7. sea cucumber
8. dungeness crab
9. octopus
10. sand dollars
11. clams and cockles
12. pacific spiny lumpsucker
13. caprellid amphipod
14. stalked jellyfish
15. eelgrass isopod
16. juvenile salmon
17. bubble shell
18. opalescent nudibranch
19. perch
20. juvenile kelp crab
21. alabaster nudibranch
22. scallop
23. gunnel
24. bay pipefish
25. sea urchin
26. juvenile sculpin
27. decorator crab
28. juvenile clams
29. juvenile flounder and sole
30. juvenile crab
31. geoduck
32. sediment microfauna
33. snail and snail eggs
34. juvenile cod, tomcod, and wall-eyed pollock
35. herring eggs
36. jellyfish
37. larval fish
38. meliba – hooded nudibranch
39. tubesnout
40. shrimp
41. brooding anemone
42. prickleback
43. sculpin
44. bacteria on detritus

45. moonsnail
46. sunflower seastar
47. sea pen
48. red rock crab

49. hermit crab
50. worms
51. ghost shrimp
52. sand lance

53. black brant
54. Canada goose
55. bufflehead

Laura Hendricks, who was at that meeting, received a copy of the draft, and, based on the meeting discussion, handwrote in her copy of the document: "(They decided to take out)."

That language was indeed dropped from subsequent drafts, and Hendricks was chastised for sharing the earlier revealing draft.

As part of an apparent strategy to turn the public against duckgrass, the Pest Plan calls for a study to characterize duckgrass as having a negative impact, followed by an effort to educate the public of this point of view, which would include adverse impacts on ecology, wildlife, marine organisms ... and shellfish production. Finally, it calls for an estimate of how much money is lost by the shellfish industry that could be attributed to duckgrass.

The state and federal government already allow shellfish operations to adversely impact the ecologically significant and supposedly beloved, native eelgrass, *marina*.

Now, the Pest Plan called for studies to determine how much *marina* was really needed. "We all know that the oyster growers would like to get rid of *Zostera marina* as well, although can't do it overtly because it is still a protected species," one person wrote in an email to Ecology in 2012.

The shellfish companies argued that the burrowing shrimp could harm *marina*. But the truth is, shrimp don't adversely affect established beds of *marina*. They can, however, colonize a *disturbed marina bed*... such as beds cut with blades, raked over with a harrow, and dredged. On the contrary, *marina* and duckgrass can move into a shrimp bed, a fact that didn't serve the anti-burrowing shrimp argument.

Having long argued that killing crab was good for crab (as part of the shrimp spraying program), and that replacing native shrimp with non-native oysters was better for the environment, the industry now recommended that the public and regulatory agencies needed to be "educated" about how non-native shellfish could provide habitat of equivalent value to the native eelgrass, paving the way for its "management."

1996 infrared photo of aquaculture activities in eelgrass beds in Samish Bay.
The yellow ochre area is vegetation—eelgrass.
(Source: Department of Natural Resources)

The Pest Plan says that the native algae, sea lettuce and eelgrasses, are major problems. It reduces these ecologically vital aquatic plants to ... weeds. The recommended control of algae and eelgrasses is to sweep them from the nets placed over the geoduck and clam farms, or to harrow the tidelands to rid them of these native plants.

According to the Pest Plan, other Major Pests include native perch, seagulls, crows, ravens, and waterfowl. Hazing the birds; blocking the birds from their native habitat by installing large wildlife "exclusion" nets over clam farms; and killing the birds ... are how birds are managed. But don't ducks and other shorebirds belong on the shoreline? Isn't this where they get the food they need to survive? One shellfish company writes that they keep native birds away from their habitat by "...harassment, hazing, and hunting are conducted," and portrays these as good environmental practices in a document entitled, "Environmental Code of Practices."

Bald Eagle trapped in Wildlife Exclusion netting that prevents wildlife from accessing their habitat

Herring trapped in netting

Shellfish Company employees installing Wildlife Exclusion netting

Bird killed by Wildlife Exclusion netting

The industry Pest Plan makes no mention of a study conducted in 1996 that found a "net decrease in total shorebird use" in areas developed for oyster farms. Instead, the industry Pest Plan casts the native birds as the pest. The five-year study conducted in California's Tomales Bay found a net decrease in total shorebird use in oyster farms, and this did not take into consideration additional stressors like hazing, harassing, or killing. Since oyster farm workers were present 62 percent of the time that the authors conducted their bird counts, the authors wondered to what extent the worker's presence also affected the shorebirds.

Along with industry themes of: more tidelands to spray in Willapa Bay and Grays Harbor; the theory that killing crabs is good for crabs; that alien oysters provide better habitat than native shrimp; and that farmed alien shellfish could replace the ecosystem function of the eelgrasses, they now took another leap and recommended a density study of the native birds, waterfowl, crows, ravens and seagulls.

For what future purpose? Would it be to build evidence that just like they successfully argued against the native shrimp—with no study or proof—there were too many native birds?

Finally, the Pest Plan recommends an investigation into how the industry can be compensated for pest damage.

INDUSTRY PEST: LAURA HENDRICKS

The Pest Plan is silent about one of the aquaculture industry's biggest pests, the aforementioned Laura Hendricks.

Industry practices are visible to more people on Hood Canal and Puget Sound than in the sparsely populated Willapa Bay and Grays Harbor. Although people in Willapa Bay and Grays Harbor may not like what goes on there, the communities are smaller, everyone knows most everyone else, and many people are afraid of retaliation. Especially people who own a business like the two ladies who were warned to drop Larry Warnberg's oysters or lose their local supply of other seafood. Another acknowledged they'd experienced bullying behavior and for that reason, did not want to be interviewed for this book.

It's a different matter when homes look out over intensively impacted inter- and sub-tidal land, where "out of sight, out of mind" just doesn't apply. They can't miss it—the operations are in the front yard of their waterfront homes. As a result, concerned people have extensively documented industry practices on Hood Canal and Puget Sound.

Given the inter-twined shellfish industry and state, these people have turned to non-governmental organizations further from the shellfish industry's influence. Three organizations stand out: the Case Inlet Shoreline Association, Coalition to Protect Puget Sound, and the Sierra Club. The Coalition to Protect Puget Sound's website contains volumes of information about the Washington State shellfish industry including graphic photographs of practices that impact the nearshore environment and native animals, as well as photos of impacts on inter- and sub-tidal lands.

No one is more outspoken in Washington State about the reach of the shellfish industry and its impacts on the environment than Laura Hendricks, the shellfish industry's arch nemesis. Laura is the common thread among the above three non-governmental organizations. She was following the development of the various Pest Plan versions and wrote about the Plan (which of course, did not officially include her) and industry practices in a guest article for an Olympia area publication:

> Unlike the gardens we plant each year, our native animal and plant species cannot be grown from a seed, bought at a store, or transplanted from stock from a neighbor. Far too many citizens in South Puget Sound have been watching large shellfish companies expand using industrial methods that are removing/destroying our native animal and plant species and dredging tidelands that eliminate the prey species for native species, including salmon.

Laura wrote that native species were drawn to the planted shellfish, which were the equivalent of a marine feedlot, and then removed, destroyed, or harassed.

> Starfish are piled up, covered with lime, or injected with bleach; sand dollars are removed from their beds and left on the upper beach to die; crabs are being dismembered; moon snails are tossed like baseballs above the banks; and masses of adorable scoter ducks are being shot and left to die on the shorelines. Essential marine vegetation is being raked up and carted away. Eagles have been seen caught in geoduck feedlot nets, left to drown if they cannot free themselves.

CHAPTER 16: THOSE PESKY PESTS

Laura found this disturbing, including the formalization of these practices in two documents entitled, "2015 Goals and Priorities," and "Pest Management Strategic Plan for Bivalves in Washington and Oregon," She wrote that the otherwise beloved native animals were portrayed as "toss-aways," and the essential marine vegetation characterized as "weed" in the latter document.

Now a leading critic of the shellfish industry, back in 2006 Laura knew very little about it. She received a surprise notice that a geoduck operation was in the permit process. The operation was to take place in front of her Henderson Bay house—on twelve tideland acres, including some of Laura's property. As she worked to resolve the question of the tideland ownership, she was struck by the details of the geoduck farm proposal.

The equipment included 500,000 PVC tubes that would fill the tidelands, and hundreds of 30x40 feet of extremely heavy nets that float on the high tide and trap animals on the way back down on the low tide.

This netting was intended to exclude native animals from the tidelands. Not only does it prevent animals from accessing their habitat, it kills them. But, geoducks are valuable, and bring upwards of $100 per pound in the lucrative Asian market.

Laura was appalled. It seemed like pollution to her, highly disruptive to the tideland and shoreline ecosystem. It also didn't jive with the high-profile work of the Puget Sound Partnership, and its efforts to restore Puget Sound. What was going on? When she attended a state meeting on aquaculture, she asked, "How can you allow this?" The silence was profound. No one rose to answer her question. "You could have heard a pin drop," she said in an interview for this book.

A man approached her during a break, and agreed to meet her privately. He gave her a name of a retired employee. She called the man. Quite elderly at that time, he advised her that corruption permeated all levels of government. Most importantly, he advised her that she needed to be careful. "He gave me the rundown on what was going on, all the dirty dealings, how far it went into government, the mafia connections, the Asian gangs in Canada and their aquaculture dealings. He told me that they were most dangerous. It wasn't too long after that I started looking at aquaculture studies. I connected with one clam research scientist who was doing research that was not good for the industry. This was my third encounter with someone threatened by the shellfish industry. This researcher told me that they went after her professionally to discredit her and put the kibosh on her research grants." They were successful in getting her called up for academic misconduct, which didn't stick.

The researcher kept on going in spite of the oppression, and so did Laura. After Laura resolved her tideland ownership issue, she almost dropped the entire shellfish industry matter. But her son wouldn't let her. "I'm Texan. On top of that, I'm Irish," she explained. "My son chastised me for backing down. He said there was obviously something terribly wrong here and he thought giving up was uncharacteristic of me. He was right."

Next, Laura went out on a boat trip hosted by another citizen group that had been fighting mussel rafts in Puget Sound since 1996. They toured farm-intense Totten Inlet, between Olympia and Shelton, on a low tide. There was a flurry of wildlife activity as they approached the Inlet, but that soon changed. "Once we turned down Totten Inlet, I was absolutely shocked by the beaches full of tubes, nets, and no birds—compared to the beaches we saw on the way there," Laura said. "The beaches were shiny; they were slick from the scraping-off of shells and sand dollars. There was nothing there. I was mortified. Then I saw the industry-suspended mussel rafts with millions of invasive species called tunicates attached and hanging off them. These tunicates now proliferate throughout Totten Inlet."

CHAPTER 16: THOSE PESKY PESTS

"As shellfish farmers, we're in business with Mother Nature,"
Pacific Coast Shellfish Growers Association website.

Example of industrial oyster farm with oysters growing in bags

Laura continued. "After that, I started calling everyone I could find. I found that 99 percent of people I contacted were scared to talk. People at UW, Sea Grant, Ecology, F&W—it didn't matter. Then I learned that Pierce County, where I live, was taking a cue from the state agencies and appeared to be brainwashed in thinking that aquaculture was not only harmless, but had environmental benefits. This is because the shellfish industry had been so successful in getting appointed to every relevant committee and into every state agency. To this day, the shellfish industry cannot produce a legitimate study supporting their claims that mono-crop farmed shellfish improve water quality. But that is their mantra."

"Pacific Coast Shellfish Growers Association members are committed to protecting their bays and estuaries to ensure a healthy supply of sustainably-produced shellfish far into the future!" According to their website.

Geoduck farm before Wildlife Exclusion nets applied

Laura found quite the opposite—oysters weren't improving water quality, they were making it worse. "It's astounding the amount of plastic they put out there. They use High Density Polyethylene netting that is really bad because it absorbs pollutants, and the marine animals eat it. When it gets into the animal's stomachs, the toxins are released into their bodies. Charles Moore calls them 'poison pills.'"

Charles Moore, oceanographer and sea captain, works to bring attention to the Great Pacific Plastic Patch, a floating toxic deathtrap of plastic in the Pacific Ocean, twice the size of Texas. Moore testified at public meetings in Washington State about the dangers of plastics, particularly HDPE plastic, but according to Laura, he was soundly ignored.

42,500 PVC pipes per acre. About eight miles of plastic pipe

Crabs get caught under the Wildlife Exclusion nets or are unable to reach their habitat as a result of being excluded from the beach

In 2012, DFW staff, who are not allowed to regulate commercial aquaculture, made some comments to Pierce County, hoping to get their concerns addressed in the Pierce County shoreline permit for an aquaculture proposal. One said, "And for goodness sake, try to get them to avoid clam predator netting. That stuff alters habitat more than you could imagine, and ends up washed all around the beach. It's just bad stuff. We do not use it on our public shellfish beaches any longer."

These concerns did not go over well with the shellfish industry according to an anonymous DFW source.

Even scientists outside state agencies who spoke out did so at risk. One scientist who testified for Laura's group put it this way when asked if "blackballed" was an accurate characterization of their treatment: "We were personally and professionally attacked; our credibility and expertise was questioned. It is certainly interesting that prior to our involvement, some of us were considered experts in our respective fields, being asked to serve on numerous technical advisory panels and committees, until we challenged the aquaculture industry. I believe that our involvement has had an impact on how some view us now, and that has likely impacted our involvement in certain work endeavors. So, is this being blackballed? Possibly."

Another scientist who testified against aquaculture's practices did not want his name mentioned in this book out of fear of retaliation.

"These guys took a lot of heat testifying for us," Laura said. "They were the only guys who would speak up."

CARBARYL ON PUGET SOUND?

Laura and DNR employees heard reports, including from shellfish company owners and shoreline residents, of carbaryl spraying in Puget Sound. "In about 2008, after I had been researching and networking for about a year, I started to hear about the carbaryl spraying—not on Willapa Bay—but here on Puget Sound," Laura said. Since her activities were getting noticed, people started to call her with information.

She would take their information and oftentimes go out and meet with them. "I went to beaches where even the sandfleas were dead, and these weren't aquaculture sites, they were just nearby. But that's not all. I noticed another pattern. People from all over the region ... from Eld, Totten, Hammersly, and Case Inlets—people who did not know one another—told me that their cats were dying. They called their cats 'beach cats' because they would go down to the beach and eat crabs and other things. But they started to die, along with everything else on the beaches."

One Puget Sound waterfront owner interviewed for this book, and whose name is withheld for privacy reasons, says she became increasingly disturbed about shellfish farming practices starting with garbage. She started filling large bags with garbage, mainly loose wildlife exclusion plastic netting, yellow rope, and labels printed with the company's information, that she found on her property and along the shoreline. She was also disturbed by the shooting of diving ducks and the spent shells.

She had heard reports of use of carbaryl in Puget Sound. Then one day, she walked by a shellfish company truck parked at her driveway while the workers were out on one of the lowest tides of the year, and saw bags of carbaryl in the back. She took photos and sent these to Laura Hendricks. "I was very active over a three-year period to get harmful shellfish farming practices stopped, attending government meetings, talking to others, and writing, but this conflict started to change my personality, so I stopped," she said.

Shellfish company work truck on Puget Sound with carbaryl in back

Two small commercial shellfish growers, who don't know each other, provided Laura with information. "Both of them told me that it was common practice in Puget Sound to use carbaryl. They say others in the industry laugh at them when they talk about how long it takes to move crab and starfish off their plots; they tell them to just use carbaryl."

The groups that Laura Hendricks is affiliated with—the Coalition to Protect Puget Sound Habitat, and the Case Inlet Shoreline Association—have websites that serve as the only on-line repository of documented shellfish industry environmental, habitat, and animal abuses. There's no industry spin or influence evident at these non-state websites.

In contrast, Ecology's aquaculture webpage seems more like a marketing site. There are no pictures of dead or dying burrowing shrimp. There are no pictures of the millions of baby, juvenile, or adult Dungeness crab killed annually in the coastal bays. No pictures of thousands of birds and shorebirds feeding on dead and poisoned dying animals. Instead, the Ecology site has pictures one would expect to see in a promotional brochure. If being truthful, could Ecology's website really paint such a rosy picture?

Eagle caught in Wildlife Exclusion netting that prevents wildlife from accessing their habitat

Ecology's website declares aquaculture a priority shoreline use, and says that aquaculture has been a part of the Pacific Northwest for thousands of years. Truthfully, is Native American harvest of wild oysters and clams the same as dense cultivation of mono-crop species in intense operations that involve cutting the eelgrasses, harrowing, grading, compacting and filling, and dredging the tidelands, removing all rocks, removing sand dollars, removing burrowing shrimp with toxic pesticides, killing crab, starfish, and birds?

COOL, CLEAN WATERS

Further, the Ecology website claims: "Bivalves coming from Washington's cool clean waters are prized by residents and others around the world."

Cool, clean waters? Ecology issues pesticide permits to the Shellfish Association for annual spraying that goes back to 1963. State studies revealed extended carbaryl residency in water and sediments, and presence of carbaryl of unknown origins at various times of the year. Cool, clean waters? Ecology received complaints of illegal pesticide use, and acknowledged it did not have the resources or expertise to monitor the Shellfish Association's annual carbaryl spraying.

On the contrary, the state said in 2012, "Willapa Bay oysters have not been chemical free since humans began using gasoline-powered watercraft and cars a hundred years ago," in a lawsuit against Fritzi Cohen when she tried to prevent spraying spartina with pesticides on her property. Fritzi was trying to keep the waters clean, so the state evidently decided to argue they were already polluted, and even referred to Willapa Bay as a "chemical soup."

Cool, clean waters? EPA's limited environmental assessment around the Shoalwater reservation revealed cause for concern for health problems—including water pollution. Cool clean waters? The Coalition to Protect Puget Sound and the Case Inlet Shoreline Association websites include photos of shellfish operation garbage; harvesting of geoduck with high pressure hoses that liquefy the soils; dead fish trapped in the netting; bald eagles caught in exclusion netting; and pictures of starfish poisoned with lime. Cool, clean waters?

Is Ecology or DFW able to protect native habitat and species from industrial-scale mono-crop shellfish farming?

In the meantime, others keep trying. In 2009, "(name removed) took the time to speak out, and the Coalition to Protect Puget Sound

Habitat and the Case Inlet Shoreline Association uploaded that person's letter. In that letter to DNR and Mason County elected Commissioners, (name removed) wrote a heartfelt plea:

> We have owned a home on the west side of Case Inlet for ten years. During that time, we have raised concerns about environmental abuses. The initial concern was with Mr. (name removed) who we witnessed poisoning the tidelands with 40-pound bags of lime. Specifically, during extremely low tides, (name removed) was making piles of starfish up and down the inlet and then covering the piles with pounds of lime. At that time, a gray whale had been feeding in Case Inlet for more than a month. In addition to killing the starfish and crabs, other marine life was dead and dying all around. At that time, I contacted Fish and Wildlife. We were shocked to again witness (name removed) using lime the following year…
>
> Since that time, Mr. (name removed) has leased his property to Taylor Shellfish. This commercial endeavor has grown dramatically with devastating environmental results. Football field-size beds of geoducks now run up and down Case Inlet. These fields consist of thousands of individual PVC tubes, small plastic nets used as hoods over each tube, all covered with netting held in place with rebar. The beach is littered with PVC pipe, nylon nets, rubber bands, rubber gloves, etc. Starfish are all but gone, as are most forms of tidal marine life. The tidelands themselves are changing—the sand is more compact, lacking the natural affects from crab, worms, and other marine life…

Unfazed, the state and industry ploughed on. To further institutionalize the industry's designation of species (mostly native) that they claim are Major Pests, the USDA paid the industry's Pacific Shellfish Institute to develop an identification guide to all these pests, detailing how destructive they are to the industry.

SIERRA CLUB INFILTRATOR

While the shellfish industry disparages native species in the Pest Plan and government-sanctioned pest guidebook and identification key, Robin Downey, the head of the Pacific Coast Shellfish Growers Association, had this to say about Laura in a letter to David Dicks, Executive Director of the Puget Sound Partnership public agency:

> On October 28, 2009, you received a letter from the Sierra Club regarding the Puget Sound Partnership's (PSP) legislative agenda. Referenced in that letter was the Partnership's agenda item calling for a moratorium on shoreline armoring and overwater structures in feeder bluff and forage fish-spawning areas. **The Sierra Club, at the behest of Laura Hendricks, who has infiltrated the organization and currently serves as aquaculture subcommittee chair**, has requested that shellfish aquaculture be included in the PSP moratorium because it "fits the same criteria." *(Emphasis added)*
>
> This is not a factually accurate claim. We are concerned that the Sierra Club is being duped to promote the narrow, anti-shellfish farming agenda of Laura Hendricks and her group, and is doing so based on the Hendricks' authored document "The Social and Environmental Impacts of Industrial Aquaculture in Washington State." This pseudo-scientific paper is based on unfounded personal opinion with a gross misrepresentation of science that is intentionally deceptive.
>
> While it is certainly true that all forms of agriculture, including shellfish aquaculture, do have impacts on natural systems, the conclusions that Hendricks tries to lead readers to in this document are unfounded and not supported by scientific literature. In an attempt to influence public policy, Hendricks and the Sierra Club employ five tactics in the document to give their personal opinion and scientific misrepresentation the air of legitimacy. These tactics are:

1) The use of misleading information or the use of partial information.

2) The selective use of unrelated scientific quotes to imply environmental harm.

3) The blatant misrepresentation of scientific data.

4) The use of unsubstantiated claims of ecological disturbance.

5) A disregard of studies that don't support their conclusions.

Ironically, she accused Laura of using the same tactics the Shellfish Association was accused of deploying in the carbaryl environmental documents time and time again.

Follow The Money

"The shellfish industry continues to target Puget Sound's most pristine areas for aquaculture," wrote Curt Puddicombe, a Case Inlet Shoreline Association Board Member, in a 2009 plea for funds to stop the shellfish industry's expansion into native habitat.

> Case Inlet is a primary target for aquaculture expansion. Their methods include scraping, contouring, and dredging the tidelands, removing (often killing) natural habitat in the areas to be planted, re-routing natural streams, spraying chemical pollutants, covering tidelands with predator nets and oyster bags, installing toxic PVC piping, rebar stakes, and fencing. All of the above is done with the industry claiming it is 'good for the environment' while there is little or NO peer-reviewed scientific research to back their claims. ... Citizens living near aquaculture farms have observed significant decreases in diversity of native species and water clarity.

But instead of stopping expansion, state and federal agencies continue to fund customized studies to help build what is called a scientific basis for expansion of the aquaculture industry into the fragile nearshore environment, and studies to boost production. These intensive monoculture operations displace native species, as acknowledged in the shellfish industry and state Pest Plan, but are characterized as higher priority.

Another example was a federal grant to conduct a study along with Taylor Shellfish's Bill Dewey, who also owns tidelands. The purpose of the study was to document differences between hand harvest of non-native manila clams versus use of a tractor on the tidelands to harvest the clams. The study, led by the industry's Pacific Shellfish Institute (where Dewey served as President), concluded that mechanical harvesting of non-native manila clams with a tractor on the tideflats had less impact than hand harvesting. Taylor Shellfish then invested in tractors to use on the tideflats because, as reported in an article entitled, "How One Family Built a Shellfish Empire On Puget Sound." "It can do the work of five or six people in half the time."

The public also paid the industry's Pacific Shellfish Institute, UW, and Taylor Shellfish, to develop human-altered geoducks for mono-crop farming in a study called "Biosecure Domestication of Native Geoduck Clams." Biosecure Domestication? The study was about how to alter clams to make them sterile.

Even while expanding large-scale mono-crop operations into existing native habitats, and even while actively spraying pesticides into marine waters, shellfish companies continue to portray their shellfish as healthy and harvested from pristine waters. They market themselves as the advocates and guardians for water quality.

Tractor in the Tidelands re-contouring the sediment

In *Willapa Bay Oysters*, narrator and WSU Professor Glenn Johnson says, "This is THEIR story, through THEIR eyes." No photos of ten million dead aquatic animals. No mention of the adverse impacts of the conversion of native habitat for non-native oysters or clams. No mention of individuals sprayed with carbaryl and suffering epilepsy that they attribute to involuntary exposure to carbaryl. An industry-told story, sponsored by shellfish companies, but with "post production" costs paid for by the public via the UW Sea Grant Program and WSU.

Johnson goes on to say, "This is the story about a 160-year-old industry that has been exploited, altered, and ultimately nurtured to a point of sustainability ... at the heart of this industry are oyster farmers and processors who, with great pride and dedication, produce one of the healthiest oysters in one of the most productive growing regions in the world. Each with their own histories, and driven by their own perspectives and interests. This unique community of oyster growers shares a passion for protecting and preserving the environment. They are dedicated to their farms and their community."

One oyster company owner added her perspective in *Willapa Bay Oysters*. "It feels good to produce a natural, sustainable food product. In this day and age when our natural resources are all getting depleted, we're actually enhancing the environment, and getting a good product out there. It feels good."

CHAPTER 17: NEONIC

Warning! Imidacloprid will be applied for burrowing shrimp
control on (date) on commercial shellfish beds
at the following locations (X).
Do not Fish, Crab, or Clam
within one-quarter mile of the treated area!
Do not harvest shellfish within 30 days after treatment!

On October 24, 2014 Ecology issued an environmental analysis prepared by the Shellfish Association, and a draft federal permit. If approved, helicopters would load up with imidacloprid instead of carbaryl.

The environmental analysis cited Kim Patten eighty-nine times as the primary scientist conducting pesticide studies. According to Patten, imidacloprid is a lot "safer, gentler, and kinder than carbaryl." Ecology relied on his research and studies, even though earlier that year Patten had publicly commented to Ecology, both as a shellfish grower and as a WSU scientist... which the state ethics board later cited in its ethics investigation of Patten.

People had forty-five days to digest the 246-page environmental analysis and this was not just any analysis. This was prepared by the Shellfish Association.

State and federal fisheries staff were, by now, so cynical that their expectations for Ecology were very low, as evident in this email exchange. Federal employee: "Unfortunately, given the personnel working this issue, my expectations on how Ecology might respond are very low. Honestly, I think they have their head in the mud and are going to go ahead and issue the permit come hell or high water ... At a minimum, I would expect to see Ecology's responses to our comments in their SEPA required "Response to Comments" document. That will be an interesting read."

State employee: "I suspect Ecology will issue the permit regardless of the comments they receive."

The claims made in the documents caused uproar by numerous people, starting with Trina Bayard, Director of Bird Conservation for Washington Audubon, who routs out:

> The idea that imidacloprid use to suppress burrowing shrimp populations will result in greater biodiversity is completely at odds with the biological outcomes observed in the published literature.

Ecology claimed: "The objective of the proposed action (spraying imidacloprid or carbaryl) is to preserve and maintain the beneficial uses of Willapa Bay and Grays Harbor."

To which Larry Warnberg tirelessly commented, "It has been established ... that these estuaries have benefitted from the two varieties of native burrowing shrimp that contribute major ecosystem support as detritivores, substrate aeration, and nutrient balance."

But what about the average person? Would they know the shrimp's vital role in the fragile ecosystem? Especially if all they were reading was the material in these documents, where the authors pervasively used negative terms for the native shrimp. Terms such as pest, disrupt, cause adverse impacts, destabilize, out of control.

Unfortunately, most people don't have time to read large, difficult to follow documents like this, because in theory they rely on state agencies to protect the environment.

But only the non-state agencies and the non-governmental organizations *furthest* from the Washington State Governor's office were blunt in condemning this spraying plan.

"Ecology is clearly aware that imidacloprid is a persistent broad spectrum pesticide that will kill nearly all benthic organisms on the acreage directly treated," wrote NMFS, a federal agency. "The NMFS believes impacts to benthic prey species will be affected beyond the area to be treated, including areas where the spray has drifted, or carried offsite by tidal currents."

Audubon's Bayard said, "Despite the difficulty that the two native species of burrowing shrimp ... pose to the shellfish industry, the species are, in fact, an integral component of the benthic environment." As the draft EIS notes, "Burrowing shrimp are considered ecosystem engineers because of their ability to control and structure the benthic community."

Yet again, others attempted to step into the void—to try to protect the environment outside the established halls of power. Bayard scoffed, "The DEIS contends that a reduction in burrowing shrimp will yield beneficial impacts for eelgrass and other aspects of invertebrate biodiversity. We find this purported benefit quite puzzling since the Shellfish Association recently applied for and received a permit to control non-native eelgrass using the herbicide Imazamox."

CARBARYL; IT'S B-A-C-K

The industry-prepared documents determined there were no insurmountable adverse impacts from spraying the new chemical, imidacloprid ... *and carbaryl.*

Carbaryl. It must have been a surprise to a lot of people: carbaryl was still on the menu! The chemical that had long been contentious ... even banned in Oregon decades ago for this same use due to its indiscriminate lethality. Yep, carbaryl. The really bad chemical. The chemical so bad that narrative was emerging in 1996 that the way to get imidacloprid approved, was to compare it to carbaryl. The chemical whose application, as determined in 2009 by NMFS, adversely impacted endangered salmon and green sturgeon in these bays. Such a bad chemical, that just months prior, EPA was forced via a lawsuit to reinstate upland spray buffers, nationally, to keep carbaryl *out of salmon bearing waters*. How could Ecology continue to allow direct spraying of carbaryl into two major coastal salmon bays? Probably because it was the industry's intent to keep carbaryl on the table. All one has to do is read the Pest Plan, which clearly states as a goal to retain carbaryl permits and its EPA registration: "Retain current registration of carbaryl for burrowing ship control."

CONTAMINATION

So, according to the state and Shellfish Association, both neurotoxic pesticides are safe to put into Willapa Bay and Grays Harbor. No problem. But if imidacloprid was so safe, why did Ecology prohibit harvest of shellfish within thirty days of treatment? Ecology says that directly sprayed shellfish were not safe to eat within thirty days of treatment. Not only that, but oysters, clams, crabs, and fish within **one-quarter of a mile** from the sprayed plot are also not safe to eat. Even if they are on someone else's—or public tidelands. One-quarter of a mile?

Fish swim around a lot. Say a fish is exposed to imidacloprid on the day of spraying and you are fishing that day. Luckily, you catch it one-half mile from a spray plot. It's safe to eat! But what if moments before you caught it, it was within one-quarter mile from a sprayed plot? It would be unsafe to eat.

Indeed, the 2014 imidacloprid and carbaryl environmental analysis said that a majority of imidacloprid moved vast distances off the sprayed plot, but Ecology insisted that its dispersal wasn't approved, just directly sprayed plots. And, contrary to established evidence that carbaryl was transported hundreds of feet from where it was sprayed at killing levels of toxicity, the industry-prepared environmental analysis quotes a shellfish owner as saying, "Carbaryl is site-specific and generally stays on or close to the point of application."

Evidently, Ecology was prepared to allow extensive contamination, claiming there were no insurmountable adverse impacts from either carbaryl or imidacloprid, and the permit would be issued with built-in chemical trespass. Every state agency that commented either supported it or did not oppose. (Curiously, the Nisqually Indian Tribe, located on Puget Sound, supported the spraying of Willapa Bay and Grays Harbor with imidacloprid.)

STATE AGENCY CAPITULATION

DNR reviewed the environmental analysis and, in addition to statements they said were unsupported, they found incomplete information, omission of recent research, a vastly underestimated area of impact, appearance of a conflict of interest on the part of Kim Patten, two instances where references did not support conclusions, and contradictory claims—after all this, they did not object to its use.

The Department of Fish and Wildlife did the same... they supported the permit after a litany of concerns. The Department of Agriculture submitted a letter... with suggested edits to the documents.

The same logic is evident in the document itself:

Carbaryl is site-specific and generally stays on or close to the point of application (R. Wilson 2002); however, studies by

Felsot and Ruppert (2002) have also found detectable
concentrations of carbaryl up to 150 m (~500 ft) away from
the treatment plot one day after treatment.

While the lethal consequences beneath the water surface are
hard to see, birds are a little more visible, and imidacloprid is a
known bird killer.

EPA knew that imidacloprid was toxic to birds in 2008, because
at the same time EPA determined imidacloprid was highly toxic to
aquatic organisms, they also had reports of bird mortalities. "There
are four incidents involving imidacloprid that have been noted
reflecting lawn use and effects to non-target organisms:

1) surfaced dead grubs appeared to have been eaten by birds,
resulting in the death of several young and adult robins;

2) possible runoff event from a lawn resulted in the death of
3,000 crayfish in a nearby stream;

3) "mad bee" disease in France; and

4) & 5) lawn grass chemically burned by the application of the
compound."

The EPA staff added, "A private citizen of Myerstown, Pa.,
reported watering in pesticide (GrubEx) and then found that grubs
had surfaced a couple of days later. He was very concerned to see
that the birds that fed on the grubs died."

In this instance, upland birds ate toxic grubs then died. What
about birds that feasted on dead and dying shrimp, crab and other
aquatic organisms in the throes of imidacloprid poisoning? How
would this be any different from a robin eating a toxic grub?

To allay concerns about imidacloprid's effects on birds, Kim
Patten conducted a visual observation study of birds eating
imidacloprid-poisoned animals and determined there was no ill effect.

They didn't wobble, as far as he could see in 2013, the year before they widely sprayed the bays with imidacloprid on an "experimental basis" in 2014.[13] He reported no ill effect. They didn't seem confused. He didn't observe any paralysis.

> Birds were observed foraging on and nearby the sites following treatments. No birds exhibiting behaviors consistent with exposure to a pesticide (e.g., confusion, poor balance, paralysis) were observed (Patten, 2013).

Other scientists had a different view. Thomas McDowell from the U.S. Fish and Wildlife Service wrote:

> Willapa Bay and Grays Harbor support vitally important migratory and resident bird populations. If Ecology decides to issue the proposed permit, we expect that these waterfowl, raptor, and shorebird populations will be exposed to imidacloprid and its degradation products both on and off the treated sites.
>
> Birds that forage on the exposed tidelands will encounter and may ingest the granular pesticide product directly. Birds that forage on the exposed tidelands are also likely to ingest contaminated vegetation, sediments, and/or prey items. The western snowy plover, which is listed as threatened and uses sand and mudflats, sand islands, sand spits, and open beaches located in Grays Harbor and Willapa Bay, is likely to be exposed and affected.

Audubon's Trina Bayard shared with Ecology a long list of "not-

---

[13] The annual spraying of carbaryl directly onto oysters (initially prohibited) was also allowed as an "experiment" in 1984, and quickly became the norm even though it killed a tremendous amount of crab and was opposed by the crab industry. According to the state, no agency monitored the one-year harvest ban on sprayed oysters, and no agency routinely tested post-spray harvested species for carbaryl including clams, crab, and fish for consumer protection.

cited" studies that raised serious concerns about imidacloprid's widespread contamination of aquatic systems and associated threat to biodiversity. She also gave them references to studies that documented direct toxicity to birds.

Bayard asked Ecology to integrate recent advances in the published literature about both the short- and long-term effects of imidacloprid into the EIS, and any approved permit language. DNR staff made the same observation in their list of concerns. She also questioned their science on imidacloprid's effects on invertebrates:

> It is problematic that the first invertebrate samples did not occur until two weeks post-treatment. Samples should have been conducted within one to two days to document immediate population level effects. Such a delay likely minimizes the apparent effects of imidacloprid by allowing time for immigration of invertebrates to the site.

In 1992, and now again in 2014, the Shellfish Association and Ecology were accused of drawing conclusions not supported by cited studies. DNR staff highlighted two instances that raised this concern. In one instance, the draft environmental analysis referenced a study from which the authors concluded, "It is unlikely that there would be adverse effects to forage fish or groundfish from imidacloprid in water ... due to dilution, adsorption onto sediment, and application during low tide conditions."

Staff checked the cited study and could find no laboratory toxicity studies on forage fish.

DNR staff found another inconsistency in the discussion of eelgrass, placing inaccurate emphasis on native eelgrass instead of the non-native duckgrass as a natural deterrent to burrowing shrimp colonization. Why?

The cited study was from 2003, and its findings should have

been cause for alarm. The researchers confirmed that poisoned shrimp habitat was readily colonized by duckgrass, which they are now poisoning *(covered in final chapter)*.

In essence, the alternate poisoning of these two inter-twined species would perpetuate a never-ending toxic pesticide cycle. So, the shrimp would be killed. Then the duckgrass would move in and be poisoned. Then the shrimp would move back in. How long can this go on?

Commenting on their own proposal, the Shellfish Association requested more sediments that they could impact with their pesticides. They asked that the entirety of both Willapa Bay and Grays Harbor be included in the Sediment Impact Zone for their pesticides, not just their shellfish plots. If Ecology didn't expand the area they could pollute with state approval, they argued, southern Willapa Bay "will be vulnerable to unlimited burrowing shrimp infestations."

HOW BIG?

Out of all the DNR staff's list of concerns, one stands out: the lack of a true defined area of impact: "Key information from prior NMFS and USFWS documents is not included regarding the off-site impacts (chemical trespass) of carbaryl in the water column and sediments. Ecology does not include a map of this plume and does not quantify or illustrate these impacted areas. This trespass is likely to affect State-owned aquatic lands."

DNR staff then did something only mentioned in the past: they estimated the area likely impacted by the pesticides. First, they started with carbaryl. "The actual estimated impacted Willapa Bay acreage is between 2,900 and 34,300 acres. The actual estimated Grays Harbor acreage is between 967 and 11,433 acres." Not the 1,500 acres on Willapa Bay or the 500 acres on Grays Harbor, as claimed by Ecology and the Shellfish Association.

After completing this exercise for carbaryl, staff went on to imidacloprid. "Given the lack of reliable, objective data regarding chemical trespass of imidaclropid (sic), it is assumed that the plume is the same as for carbaryl. The extent of chemical trespass for imidacloprid or its additive effects has not yet been determined ... yet Ecology has determined no adverse effect in this DEIS," staff wrote.

DNR staff concluded their discussion:

> Ecology justifies the proposed pollution and contamination
> by characterizing it as just a small part of the overall
> Ecosystem, and without quantifying the real area of impact,
> as illustrated above. Ecology does so without taking into
> consideration the above estimated area of impact, which is in
> the range of 3,867 to 45,733 acres in both ecosystems.

CONFLICT OF INTEREST?

DNR did not object to the war on the burrowing shrimp, even after raising questions about the objectivity of Patten. They found testimony Patten gave as both a private citizen who owned a commercial clam farm wanting to kill duckgrass on his property AND, as the WSU employee conducting the studies the state relied on to poison the duckgrass. Patten's comments to the agency with the power to list the duckgrass as a noxious weed (which would open the door to poison it), include:

> Kim Patten, Ph.D., WSU long Beach Research and Extension
> Unit; As a private landowner: I find it unacceptable that I will
> be unable to control Japanese eelgrass on my own property.

Patten wanted to be able to spray his entire property, with no perimeter buffer required. In another exchange, this time with

Ecology, he argued against any "no spray buffers" around the perimeter of a tideland parcel:

> ...I would like the Department of Ecology to reconsider this buffer ... My farm: As a commercial clam grower with a small parcel of ground thickly covered by Z japonica, this buffer will prevent most of my ground from being farmed. I have a 160-foot by 200-foot parcel that is farmable (32,000 ft²). This buffer removes 16,800 ft². My ground produces ~ 0.5 lbs/ft2 every 4 to 5 years. I get paid $0.75/lb. On ground with japonica my yields have been about half. This totals approximately $5,000 to $6,000 in crop loss. I think this is an unreasonable economic impact. The ground does not have drainage swales and there is little chance of "chemical trespassing."

At the same time as these comments, Patten was negotiating a commercial lease of his tidelands with Brian Sheldon of Northern Oyster Company. In his comments to Ecology, Patten invoked the threat of a "taking" of private property: "...Not being able to treat up to the buffer zone constitutes a taking of private revenue and right to farm."

After living through spartina eradication, defoliation of eelgrass in Willapa Bay, and now a new chemical to kill shrimp, Marcial Hunter concluded, "In today's situation we have little cause for confidence that Ecology is willing or able to require an adequate EIS or to write an adequate permit for imidacloprid on burrowing shrimp."

~

And he was right. Unlike Wall Street investments where past performance is no guarantee of future results, on April 16, 2015, Ecology granted a five-year permit to the Shellfish Association to spray imidacloprid, the only place in the country where imidacloprid could be sprayed directly into the water. Ecology, seduced by the Shellfish Associations mantra of "more, more, more," upped the directly sprayed tideland acres from 800 to 2,000 acres: 1,500 in Willapa Bay, and 500 in Grays Harbor.

Meteorologist and blogger Cliff Mass was following this permit and summed up the situation:

> This issue represents a major failure by the state agency
> responsible to protect Washington's environment
> (Washington State Department of Ecology). It is an example
> of a wealthy industry getting its way, of cozy relationships
> with politicians, of incomplete information being provided to
> the State's citizens.

Chapter 18: Chef Hits Fan

E ight days after Ecology issued the imidacloprid permit to kill native shrimp, the shit hit the fan. *Bloomberg Business News* published an article written by Bill Donahue entitled: "Washington State Turns to Neurotoxins to Save Its Oysters. A pesticide from the group of chemicals linked to colony collapse disorder will now be sprayed in U.S. waters. What could go wrong?"

Then, *The Seattle Times'* Danny Westneat picked up the story and put it on the front page, above the fold. "Disbelief over state plan to spray neurotoxin into oyster beds. The state has approved plans to spray in Willapa Bay a neurotoxic pesticide that has a warning right on the bottle: 'Do not apply directly to water.' What could go wrong?"

Westneat's article set off a firestorm:

> As a retired nuclear power-plant operator, Ross Barkhurst,70, is by no means an environmentalist. In fact, he spent his career clashing with them.
>
> But even he's shocked by what just got approved in our supposedly green Washington state: They're going to use crop-dusting helicopters to spray into the oyster beds of Willapa Bay a neurotoxic pesticide that has a warning right on the bottle: "Do not apply directly to water."
>
> "I'm no greenie, but this state's going to make one out of me

yet," says Barkhurst, who lives on Willapa Bay, near South Bend. "They have no idea what this is going to do to the ecosystem. Their program is 'spray and hope.'"

The state disputes that, but surprisingly that's pretty much the conclusion of two of the biggest environmental regulators in the country, the U.S. Fish and Wildlife Service and the National Oceanic and Atmospheric Administration. Both opposed the spraying program, arguing it's experimental and could have unintended side effects on fish and other wildlife. It received the green light anyway.

Trina Bayard, the director of bird conservation at Audubon Washington, told Westneat that she got the sense the state would back the oyster growers' plan no matter what, because it's such a beloved industry.

She wrote to Ecology about how the pesticide might affect ducks in what is a major migratory flyway, but the state replied, "The potential for direct exposure of the pesticide to birds would be limited since application techniques by helicopter tend to flush birds from the target area."

Bayard told Westneat, "It kind of leaves you speechless," she said. "Their stated plan is they're going to keep the birds safe from the pesticide by flushing them first with helicopters."

Westneat reported that Rich Doenges, of Ecology, said they realized that there were a lot of concerns, but that they were confident that, "This is going to work," and that spraying is likely to begin May 17. People have until May 16 to appeal the permit to the Pollution Control Hearings Board.

Then, fourteen days after permit issuance, *The Seattle Times* ran another article, this one by their food writer Bethany Jean Clement, entitled: *Chefs 'horrified' by plan to spray pesticide on oyster beds:*

Taylor Shellfish says the pesticide is safe for use in Willapa

Bay and Grays Harbor, but Seattle eateries are scrambling to make sure the oysters they serve aren't affected. Renee Erickson was on the phone to her oyster suppliers as soon as she heard the news about Willapa Bay and Grays Harbor.

As chef/owner of several Seattle restaurants, including renowned oyster bar, The Walrus and The Carpenter, the region's famous bivalves are her bread and butter, so she was "horrified" by a newly approved plan to spray some Washington oyster beds with imidacloprid, a neurotoxic pesticide, starting as soon as low tide on May 17.

With headlines like, "Washington state turns to neurotoxins to save its oysters" (*Bloomberg*) and "Disbelief over state plan to spray neurotoxin into oyster beds" (in *The Seattle Times*), Erickson was facing dismay from patrons like the one who emailed at 6 a.m. Wednesday to say, "If this happens, I'll be boycotting all your establishments."

That dismay, as it happens, was misdirected: Erickson does not sell Willapa or Grays Harbor oysters.

But plenty of other people do.

Taylor Shellfish, a $75 million international company with more than 650 employees, is the biggest farmed-shellfish operation in the country. It worked with the Washington Department of Ecology to get approval for the pesticide use, and says it's done a lot of testing.

Owner Bill Taylor maintains the neurotoxin is safe, though its manufacturers specifically state it's not for use in water, and both the U.S. Fish and Wildlife Service and the National Oceanic and Atmospheric Administration have sounded the alarm about unknown consequences.

Taylor says his company and the Department of Ecology have been "trying to look at environmental effects on other species" of imidacloprid since the mid-2000s, finding that the pesticide has "less effects" than the one used previously, carbaryl.

"There's been a lot of work done," Taylor says. "A lot of

rigorous work on the effect of the pesticide in the environment there. Part of the permit going forward is continuing to look at effects, various residues left after."

The permit also says oysters cannot be harvested within thirty days of spraying.

Taylor Shellfish invokes sustainable practices as part of its mission, but, as restaurateur Erickson puts it, "It's another category of farming."

And regardless of how safe spraying oysters with neurotoxic pesticide may or may not be, those aren't oysters her customers want to eat.

One day later, on Friday May 1, 2015, Ecology attempted to quell the media flurry and sway public opinion by posting on its blog what it called "facts" to set the record straight.

This is the reaction that attempt got:

Commenter Andy said…

Shame on you Dept. of Ecology. This blog post is misleading and factually incorrect. The final paragraph of your blog says your job is to protect the water and environment for all of us in Washington. Clearly this isn't true. This action benefits the Oyster growers and ONLY the oyster growers. Yes, less Carbaryl is good, but replacing one toxin with another is not the answer.

Commenter Clean Water said…

From the Govenor (sic) who gets massive in-kind donations and money from industry to Ecology, that is nothing more than a mouthpiece to industry, that would be any industry that gives to the so-called environmental Gov.

Commenter Stacia said…

The government department responsible for protecting the environment and ecology is only concerned with protecting the wealthy, and consistently values economic interests over the health of both the people and the environment. It's completely expected and the sole reason why there are so many health-conscious, environmentally concerned citizens filling the void your department leaves behind. If the DOE ever aligns itself with the majority of independent, scientific facts and the well-being of the citizens and environment you're paid to represent, you'll know ... you'll stop having to write letters like this.

Then, there was a protest outside Ecology's headquarters, calling even greater public attention to Ecology's approval to spray killer pesticides into Washington's two largest coastal bays.

Evidently, working closely and in overtime, and on a Sunday, Ecology and the Shellfish Association abruptly announced that they were jointly cancelling the permit and declared the application withdrawn, a mere seventeen days after permit issuance.

Ecology posted this press release on their blog:

"One of our agency's goals is to reduce toxics in our environment," said Governor Jay Inslee's appointed Ecology Director, Maia Bellon. "We've heard loud and clear from people across Washington that this permit didn't meet their expectations, and we respect the growers' response."

Commenter Gretchen Engle said…

Wow, I'm glad someone reminded Ecology what they are supposed to be about! There should never have been approval of such a permit, and the double speak DOE sent out about their decision exhibited their complete capitulation to industry.

But when *The Seattle Times* reporter Clement asked Margaret Barrette, executive director of the Pacific Coast Shellfish Growers Association, "What about other pesticides or herbicides?"

Barrette said, "Not really. No. Most of my members tout the fact that they don't do anything to get their crops to grow."

But Ecology had recently (April 2014) granted some of her members a five-year permit to spray Willapa Bay with imazamox, and spraying began in 2014 to kill the ecologically important duckgrass and eelgrass.

~

Commenter and meteorologist Cliff Mass was aware. Mass asked two questions. Two important questions:

1) Will DOE forbid the use of carbaryl?
2) Will DOE forbid the use of herbicides to kill eelgrass?

Thanks, Cliff Mass

Protest signs on Hood Canal after media exposure about this particular pesticide. (Source: Author)

CHAPTER 19: REALITY CHECK

"What really got us was the social media," confessed one prominent oyster company owner about the backlash over the direct helicopter spraying of 2,000 acres with imidacloprid in Willapa Bay and Grays Harbor.

Northern Oyster's Brian Sheldon said growers were "in a state of shock" over the public reaction to the media exposure. He said he had hoped growers would be perceived as being responsive to environmental concerns by using imidacloprid, and lamented the loss of $600,000 from just one thirty-acre oyster "farm" that he blamed on the native shrimp, if they couldn't kill it.

After the media fallout, they hired a public relations firm to take control of the messaging and swore that they would be back.

A poetic commenter with a funny bone posted this about *The Seattle Times* article:

> Just keep clam everyone. The world is our oyster. Taylor is not only in a stew, but in a downright pickle. Maybe they are just doing it for the halibut. This PR nightmare makes bivalves all over the Salish unsafe. Their PR guy is getting crabby and looking to bait reporters into other stories. Stay Strong *Seattle Times*!!!!! It is downright fishy!!!!!!

But only the imidacloprid permit made the papers; imazamox and the defoliation of Willapa Bay eelgrasses did not. Just as the shellfish companies sprayed during the Shoalwaters' health crisis, they kept right on killing Willapa Bay eelgrasses while the public received only the imidacloprid story, and a hired PR firm to put out the fire over that exposure. They continued to assure everyone that imidacloprid was safe, and that they were, indeed, a sustainable, pristine industry.

"Washington shellfish growers are proud of our sustainable industry. Many of our farms are operated by multi-generational family companies," said the Pacific Coast Shellfish Growers Association president in an article announcing Governor Inslee's new declaration that a week in June was now "Shellfish Week."

Governor Inslee signing Proclamation June 4, 2016 is Shellfish Week.
(Source: Associated Press)

Throughout the imidacloprid media crisis, shellfish company websites remained the same, claiming sustainable operations with oysters and clams from pristine water. A search of Taylor Shellfish Farms' website showed no results for "carbaryl," "imidacloprid," "imazamox," or "pesticide," but a search on the word "sustainable" produced products for purchase and an entire page devoted to sustainability with these announcements:

> Taylor Shellfish is also proud to announce that shellfish produced on our South Puget Sound and Willapa Bay farms have been certified by the Aquaculture Stewardship Council (ASC), a leading international third-party certifier of responsibly farmed seafood. We are working to certify all of our farms, which represent multiple unique regions of the West Coast, through the ASC program.

Their website features a statement from the head of the ASC:

> "This achievement distinguishes Taylor Shellfish as an innovator in the seafood market and is proof of their strong commitment to responsible farming and good social practices. We are thrilled they have become the first farm in the United States to join the program. The U.S. is a hugely important market in terms of global aquaculture consumption and, by partnering with industry leaders such as Taylor Shellfish, we can make a strong case that responsibly farmed fish is better for business and better for the environment." *Chris Ninnes* — **CEO of the Aquaculture Stewardship Council**

In spite of historical and planned pesticide use, ground culture mono-crop operations of a non-native oyster, including the chromosomally modified triploid oyster, routine dredging, and dumping gravel and shells into the bay, the Aquaculture Stewardship

Council (ASC) certified Taylor Shellfish Willapa Bay farms with the designation "Farmed Responsibly," a certification that the ASC says is credible, meaningful, and effective. The ASC certified these farms on March 24, 2016, three weeks after Taylor Shellfish submitted its annual Willapa Bay imazamox spray plan to Ecology (March 1, 2016) to spray imazamox onto 277 acres of Willapa Bay.

The ASC is based in Europe and is not affiliated with the USDA organic certification program. The ASC says that it is an independent, non-profit organization whose purpose is to promote best practices to minimize the environmental and social footprint of commercial aquaculture. Through its consumer label, the Council promotes certified responsibly farmed products in the marketplace. Do people buy products with this label thinking the animal came from a chemical free operation?

During the limited opportunity to comment, the Council received opposing comments and letters, including lengthy discussions of Taylor Shellfish's historical pesticide use. Marcial Hunter, Trina Bayard of Audubon Washington, Laura Hendricks of Coalition to Protect Puget Sound Habitat, and others, all raised concerns. "None of their current practices are sustainable by any stretch," a local farmer wrote.

According to the ASC, in 2016, Taylor Shellfish "... is not applying any chemicals to its farm beds." Yet Taylor Shellfish Farms sprayed imazamox in 2014 and 2015 of a five-year permit through 2018. When Marcial pointed out this annual use of the herbicide imazamox, which by common definition is a pesticide, the ASC insisted that Taylor did not use pesticides[14]. The Council also said that Taylor Shellfish "...does not farm any transgenic species or genetically engineered organism." The Council apparently decided

---

[14] He also pointed out that Taylor did not disclose in its application that Willapa Bay is critical habitat for the ESA-listed green sturgeon, on an ESA question.

dredge harvesting, which impacts the benthos, was responsible farming as well.

Even as *Bloomberg Business News* and *The Seattle Times* broke the story about the shellfish companies' imidacloprid permit, no information could be found on the spraying companies' websites about their historical use of carbaryl, or the proposed replacement, imidacloprid. (Of the following company websites, Taylor Shellfish and Coast Seafoods were also permitted, and did spray imazamox into Willapa Bay [see Appendix A]. A search of their websites for this pesticide did not produce any results.) Quite the opposite:

From the Taylor Shellfish website:

> Sustainability has become an important consideration in the seafood world, and we're proud to be at the forefront of that movement. By drinking the waters they live in all day long, and building their bodies out of the nutrients in those waters … excellent water quality….

Coast Seafood's website doesn't mention any of these pesticides either.[15] Instead:

> Coast Seafoods' oysters are pampered from infancy and are harvested on our 14,000+ acres of pristine State-Certified Pacific Coast Tidelands. In the states of Washington and California, the water quality in coastal estuaries is continually monitored for harmful pollutants. Should a pollution event occur, the oyster beds are closed to harvest until tests reveal the oysters are pollution-free and safe to eat. These two states have the highest water quality standards in the country.

---

[15] See Appendix A for a list of companies permitted to use various pesticides.

CHAPTER 19: REALITY CHECK

Neither does Bay Center Mariculture website mention pesticide use:

> The rich intertidal waters of Willapa Bay produce shellfish
> known the world over for quality and cleanliness.

Or Ekone Oyster's website:
> Our fresh-shucked oysters and smoked oysters are harvested
> from the pristine Willapa Bay estuary.... In order to produce
> the finest tasting oyster, we have to be responsible stewards
> of the environment where the oysters grow. Water quality is
> vital to growing healthy shellfish.

Or Goose Point Oyster's (Nisbet Oyster) website:
> As good stewards of Willapa Bay estuary, we've been
> farming exceptional oysters for decades. Luckily for you, we
> oyster farmers produce healthy, plump, oysters year-round.
> The highest level of quality, food safety, and pure distinctive
> Pacific flavor is our promise to you in every order.

The Pacific Coast Shellfish Growers Association website features their Environmental Policy:

> As shellfish farmers, we're in business with Mother Nature.
> The way we see it, keeping things natural is the key to our
> success. Throughout our growing areas in ... Washington ...
> clean water and environmentally sound farming practices
> produce the finest quality shellfish in the world.

They say:

> The unique stewardship role of shellfish farmers, long-time
> champions for water quality, is beneficial to every water user.
> Shellfish farmers in the Pacific Coast Shellfish Growers
> Association recognize that long-term sustainability depends
> on the broader overall environmental health of the estuaries

in which they work and recognition of respect for and among other estuary users.

After the public backlash and media flurry from May 2015 settled down, the Shellfish Association reapplied to use imidacloprid to kill shrimp on January 8, 2016, and Ecology re-issued the 2014 imidacloprid and carbaryl environmental analysis in October 2017, with some modifications. According to Ecology, the Shellfish Association submitted its application on behalf of a group of about a dozen growers, but when asked in an email for a list of those companies, Ecology said they didn't know who they were.

The Coastal Watershed Institute commented, resenting what they called the "withdraw, wait, and resubmit permit strategy," arguing that the public was not well served by having to re-iterate points and re-submit reviews that insisted public agencies do their jobs.

Ecology received hundreds of comments on the resurrected permit, the majority of which were vehemently opposed to the spraying. Again, people raised serious concerns about gaps in data, acknowledged uncertainties, uncited claims, conclusions not supported by available evidence, selective information, "curious statements," and about Kim Patten's objectivity given that he had been found by the state ethics board to have a conflict of interest. The list goes on.

The Center for Food Safety, a national non-profit fighting to empower people, support farmers, and protect the environment from industrial food production, joined with the Center for Biological Diversity and the Western Environmental Law Center to write yet another scathing formal comment in the long history of people, organizations, and agencies trying to stop shellfish industry use of pesticides. In their twenty-two page letter, with references totaling 633 pages, they documented what they called Field Study Flaws and

Gaps and accused the researchers (one of which they pointed out had a conflict of interest) of cherry picking data.

They conclude that given the many unknowns, lack of data, under-estimated negative ecosystem impacts, and substantively inadequate environmental review, Ecology instead must focus on habitat restoration and restore balance to these bays.

Others also formally commented on the proposed permit:

Lyn De Danaan: Oh, please. I can't even be sane in my response. Haven't we been here before ... a thousand times ... with the wishy-washy assessment that there is "no known impact"?

Matthew Hart: I will try and keep this civil, but I must say it is difficult. You are talking about spraying pesticides directly into a bay of the Pacific Ocean, to appease a single oyster company? Are you kidding me? There are known, direct impacts, on a variety of invertebrates that are food for the salmon we depend on in the Pacific Northwest. This is based on your own supplemental environmental review. This has to be the most absurd idea I've ever heard. Please exercise some common sense and tell these jerks from the Shellfish Association to go to hell.

Lisa Belleveau: I do NOT support the use of pesticide in the estuaries of Willapa or Grays Harbor! I commented against this a couple years ago and the permit was withdrawn, just to have them try to push it through again! I do NOT approve of the killing of a native species, via poisoning the ecosystem, so that a non-native oyster can flourish! Imidacloprid will kill more than just the target invertebrate and cause damage to these delicate estuarine systems.

Larry Warnberg dusted off his 2014 opposition letter and sent it in, but this time, his call was matched by another oyster grower to the north. His lone voice as a former grower opposed to pesticides was matched by a Grays Harbor grower. Erika Buck of FMO AquaCulture wrote, "Please stop—there is no reason to issue a permit for the chemical control of ghost shrimp." She encouraged Ecology to take a harder look at the oyster-growing practices that create shrimp habitat, including the use of miles of nylon rope on plastic poles that impede incoming currents and promote the accumulation of sediment, creating perfect habitat for shrimp, and invited them to come visit her pesticide-free operation.

More public comments rolled in on the proposed permit:

Anonymous Anonymous: Are you crazy?! NO!

Todd Tanner: Hi, I'm an outdoor writer as well as a seafood lover. If you folks decide to spray toxic crap on shellfish beds, I can guarantee you that I'll be writing stories about the fact that no one in the U.S. should eat Washington oysters. Lord, what an incredibly stupid idea. Please do not use pesticides on your shellfish beds. There's enough toxic crap in our marine environments already. Don't make it worse.

Robert Nerenberg: I'm not interested in eating shellfish exposed to a chemical that DOE thinks about in this way: "There are still knowledge gaps about imidacloprid. Further research is needed." I don't want to be a test subject and will immediately stop eating Washington oysters if this is allowed.

In a briefing before the DFW Commission, Patten (WSU scientist and private shellfish farmer) said that imidacloprid causes "some reduction of some species, after fourteen days, they all recover; after twenty-eight, no big deal." And, contrary to the environmental analysis that imidacloprid spread at least one-half mile from a sprayed site he told them, "It doesn't go very far," and has "No off-site impacts," and they "Basically found no drift in the water."

In the meantime, baby oysters and shrimp build their tiny shells—a fragile armature against a crazy world.

CHAPTER 20: NO DUCKGRASS ... NO DUCKS

When Marcial gave Kim Patten ten frozen wigeon gullets full of duckgrass a few months prior, he held back twenty others. "I didn't trust him," he said.

When the tide comes in, the water lifts the blades of eelgrass and suspends them like an underwater grass meadow. Glance into an underwater meadow of eelgrass, and animals glance back. Eelgrass beds are living communities, full of life-preserving shelter, blades of grass on which to lay eggs, and blades of grass and roots to eat. Their contribution to the ecosystem is multifaceted. Eelgrass is not a weed.

On the contrary, in Puget Sound, eelgrass is in such steep decline that patches of what remain are cherished and protected ... except on monoculture shellfish sites where eelgrass is considered a weed by the growers. When the tide recedes, the water drops the eelgrasses back onto the tideflats, where they cover vulnerable animals from predators. Flip back a patch of grass, a crab peeks back, then scurries to hide.

The shellfish companies identified in their 2010 Pest Plan two species of eelgrass—duckgrass and *marina*—that they considered pests. Marcial and other waterfowl experts know that duckgrass of Willapa Bay is the primary food source for ... ducks. Ducks don't eat *marina*.

Because waterfowl feed in areas where they are threatened by predators, it's often advantageous for the birds to "eat and run." Consequently, waterfowl have extra storage capacity in their esophagus, which enables the birds to carry considerably more food from foraging areas than they could otherwise eat. The duck esophagus is capable of expanding to accommodate substantial amounts of food. Dissecting a bird's upper digestive system, which many refer to as the "gullet," reveals what the bird recently ate. American wigeon, northern pintail, and mallard are the three main species of ducks that eat duckgrass on Willapa Bay. Marcial found in his research that these ducks are dependent on duckgrass to survive. In fact, the wigeon's diet consists of more plant matter than any other dabbling duck. The Northern Pintail is considered a common bird in steep decline. The Dusky, a goose, eats both duckgrass and *marina*, and on paper, the Dusky is a protected goose, due to low a population.

Based on years of hunting and meticulous research, Marcial knows that the Pacific Brant goose (Brant), which looks like a miniature Canada goose, eats duckgrass and *marina*. "When I examine the gullets of Brant, there are pellets of *marina* eelgrass, alternating with small pellets of duckgrass," he explained. "The Brant eat both." Historically, Willapa Bay had large populations of spring staging Brant as they headed north, where female Brant fatten up on the grasses. They need this food to form their young and to fly north in the spring.

Duck dependency on duckgrass, and goose dependency on both grasses is not breaking news to the scientists and habitat managers of Willapa Bay. Others know ducks rely on duckgrass because they lobbied hard to spray spartina with chemicals to protect duckgrass. "Save the Birds!" was their battle cry to eradicate spartina. And it worked. Agriculture led a massive glyphosate and imazapyr spray program for over two decades. In 2011, nearing the end of the spartina eradication program, Patten said, "It's been a 'spiritual experience' watching the birds come back to the mudflats."

Ducks over duckgrass in Willapa Bay

Even as he stood on the shores having his spiritual experience, Patten was working with the shellfish growers on a plan to poison duckgrass. Both duckgrass and *marina* are problematic for the non-native clam and oyster farms. The shellfish companies say the duckgrass is getting too thick in the upper inter-tidal to grow fat clams, threatening the lucrative $5 million non-native commercial clam industry on Willapa Bay. And, not only that, it is impacting their oyster growing areas too. They say the duckgrass is providing a place for predators (to their non-native shellfish) to hide, and that it was even displacing the endangered green sturgeon ... the same green sturgeon subjected to carbaryl-laced water passing over their gills and killing their main forage item—burrowing shrimp.

The same eelgrass, they proudly proclaimed to EPA in 2002, had expanded due to their poisoning of the shrimp. But, now, the shellfish companies say they are concerned about the endangered sturgeon and the duckgrass has to go, to protect it. They even say it is adversely affecting the burrowing shrimp.

"I'm not sure how they manage to hold a straight face when they argue that the duckgrass is adversely impacting native burrowing animals like shrimp," Marcial said sheepishly.

PERPETUAL PESTICIDE CYCLE

Yet the relationship between eelgrass and burrowing shrimp by then was old news: it is difficult for shrimp to colonize an eelgrass bed, but it's easy for eelgrass to colonize a shrimp bed. So when they sprayed duckgrass, shrimp will move in. Then they would spray the shrimp, and the duckgrass would move in. Then they would spray the duckgrass ... and so on. Marcial suggested that if they were so upset about the amount of duckgrass, then they should stop spraying shrimp.

"The state uses the fact that duckgrass may be non-native, to kill it to benefit only one group: commercial non-native clam and non-native oyster growers. Duckgrass is not really an invasive species. It does not displace *marina*, and provides many of the ecological services that *marina* did before it was ripped out by dredges and buried by oyster shells. Big difference. Spartina was a disaster; duckgrass is an enhancer, and even more important because of the loss of *marina*—from shellfish operations. Now that the shellfish companies are moving into the shallows with their non-native clam culture, we really are set up for overall net loss of habitat," Marcial said with dread.

For example, as the shellfish companies dump gravel by the barge load to expand into the nearshore areas, they are obviously impacting native habitat. The purpose? To firm up the sediments to grow their non-native manila clams—the most lucrative shellfish worldwide. (Yet no state or federal regulatory agency can disclose how much gravel has been dumped onto native habitat ... or how many acres have already been converted for these invasive clams ... or how much more is planned. This is information they don't maintain or tally. Why not?)

Filling/dumping/spraying/frosting gravel into sensitive nearshore habitat to convert to non-native manila clam habitat. (Source: USACE)

The shellfish farmer's first of five steps was to convince the state to remove protections for duckgrass as a priority species. Bill Dewey of Taylor Shellfish laid out the industry's strategy in a February 2011 email to Miranda Wecker, now the powerful chair of the DFW Commission who lived on Willapa Bay, and worked for UW as the

Director of Marine Programs out of its coastal office providing support to issues important to the shellfish industry.

Dewey: "A group of us shellfish growers and the Pacific Coast Shellfish Growers Association have been working the japonica issue with Representative Blake and WDFW. I have been going back and forth with Lisa Veneroso *(author: DFW staff)* on behalf of the growers. Jim Jesernig has been working with Rep. Blake. We have been considering the RCW *(author: Revised Code of Washington)* approach and the rule amendment approach. Both have significant risks with no guaranteed outcome. Both involve public input and hearings, agency buy-in, Commission buy-in etc. Neither rule nor law specifically say protect japonica. Only through an interpretation of Zostera spp. in the hydraulic rule can one get to a position that japonica should be protected."[16] Dewey attached a letter for DFW to sign removing protection for the eelgrass *Zostera japonica*, otherwise known as "duckgrass," since it is a vital food for ... ducks. The letter properties indicated the document was authored by "billd" with Tracked Changes by Brian.

Commissioner Wecker responded to Dewey, "I think if this issue reaches the Commission, we will make the right decision."

Dewey sent the letter to Veneroso for the DFW Director's signature. Director Phil Anderson signed it.

Director Anderson, a long time charter-fishing businessman from Grays Harbor, signed the letter after coming to an understanding with the industry and their state representative. Initially, the shellfish industry asked Representative Brian Blake to introduce legislation that would require DFW to protect only one species of eelgrass: *marina*, not the duckgrass. But the industry backed away from this— it was too high profile and they didn't want people to know that their

---

[16] Conveniently, the state has determined that commercial shellfish operations are exempt from these regulations.

industry was promoting reduced protection of eelgrass in Washington State.

Instead, Anderson agreed to send the letter that he signed only to Brian Blake, as Chair of the House Agriculture and Natural Resources Committee, stating it was not DFW's intent to protect the non-native duckgrass. In internal emails, DFW staff expressed concern that if they did not remove protection for duckgrass, Representative Blake would insert unwanted language into a separate, unrelated bill important to DFW. No scientific basis was presented with DFW's decision to no longer protect duckgrass.

> Dear Chair Blake: This letter is intended to address the Washington Department of Fish and Wildlife's policy regarding the listing of the Japanese eelgrass, *Zostera japonica*, as priority habitat needing protection. We understand that the Washington State shellfish industry has been negatively impacted by this eelgrass because it occupies the same habitat that shellfish growers need to culture shellfish. This competition for space has caused some growers to lose access to valuable shellfish grounds and, therefore, they have lost, and continue to lose, economic opportunities.
>
> *Zoster japonica* is a non-native in Washington. Given this, and given the negative economic impact this aquatic plant is having on the shellfish industry, the Department will exclude *Zostera japonica* in our listing as priority habitat needing protection.

It was as easy at that. No science required. It was non-native, and it was impacting the shellfish industry. But what about its value as waterfowl food, chum salmon habitat, or herring spawning habitat—all ecological functions that put it on the protected species list in the first place? Representative Blake dismissed DFW staff's ecosystem concerns with the removal of eelgrass and particularly their concerns about waterfowl. (Early in the process, Blake indicated he wanted the DFW to go on record that the Pacific Shellfish Growers needed to control duckgrass on their properties.)

Now that the shellfish companies had duckgrass "unrecognized" by the state as a priority habitat species, they took it to the next step. They applied to have duckgrass listed as a noxious weed by the state Noxious Weed Control Board (Weed Board).

In another email from Dewey at Taylor Shellfish to the chair of the DFW Commission, Miranda Wecker, Dewey discussed getting federal support to list the duckgrass as a noxious weed. Dewey: "It was initiated at a meeting we had that NMFS was at where Steve Landino indicated they (NOAA) were looking to issue a letter in opposition to the Class C listing. We asked Steve not to take that position until he'd had a chance to see the infestation first hand through the growers' eyes. He agreed. We have a good relationship with him and can count on him to keep an open mind and form his own opinion despite what his staff might be trying to convince him."

Marcial traveled the state over a three-year period (2011, 2012, 2013) to attend hearings as the twelve-member Weed Board sought to accommodate the shellfish industry over protest from agencies, organizations, and individuals that rallied around duckgrass for its important ecological functions. The first petition to list duckgrass as a noxious weed was initiated by three shellfish interests: the Sheldons of Northern Oyster Company, another shellfish company owner, and the Pacific Coast Shellfish Growers Association. In these letters, they disparaged state agency staff who wanted to protect duckgrass, and invoked the specter of spartina by saying duckgrass was the "next spartina."

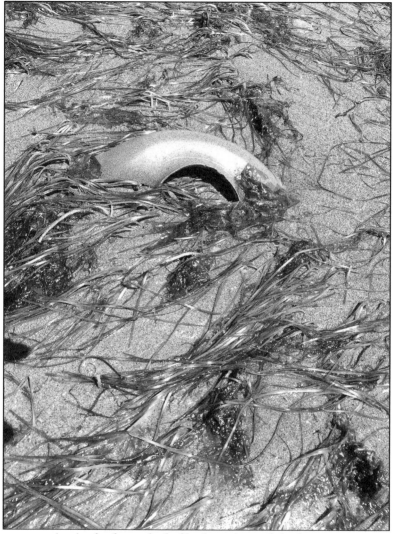

A mixed eelgrass bed of both *marina* and duckgrass.
The small crab are not visible because the eelgrass hides them, which is why
eelgrass is important habitat for crab as well as a host of other species
including juvenile salmon and the plants and animals they forage. The
round item is thousands of Moon Snail eggs encased in what is called a sand
collar. All species in this photo are considered pests of the predominantly
non-native shellfish industry. (Source: Author)

DUCKS DON'T EAT DUCKGRASS?

Weed Board staff introduced the listing in 2011, claiming that the duckgrass had numerous positive, negative, neutral, and unknown ecological impacts, but the one thing they knew for sure was that the duckgrass was causing negative economic harm to the shellfish industry because it could significantly reduce the yield of hardshell clams. Staff did not mention that these clams are non-native and invasive.

The Nature Conservancy's Lisa Younger agreed, lauding the listing of duckgrass as a great example of how the listing process had a broad enough scope to take into account economic impacts, although she didn't mention that these economic impacts were for a non-native farmed clam. "... I think this solution is actually quite elegant in that it addresses the scope of what we know and allows us to work on it...." Younger also said this proposed listing "... allows for the science to *catch up* and inform any further decisions...."[17]

When Marcial testified, he refuted the claims that the duckgrass was exploding because in his area of the bay, it had been as thick as Astroturf at low tide since the late 1970s, and according to an old-timer he knew, long before then. He argued that not only were those claims untrue, there was a problem with the industry's science. "A scientist hired by the Shellfish Association states he sampled 150 gullets and found no significant uptake of it. This is hard to imagine. I handed him ten frozen duck gullets at a public meeting last duck season with japonica in them. I told him I had twenty more. I have discussed my overall observations with him before. None of what I told him made his list of suppositions and anecdotes. Of course, what

---

[17] When asked if they were monitoring migratory waterfowl, or aware of the reported dramatic decline in waterfowl in Willapa Bay after four years of eelgrass spraying, the Nature Conservancy said they, "are not doing any work on that species."

I provided to Mr. Patten wasn't suppositions and anecdotes. It was facts and data. One can design a sampling program in a manner to preclude finding japonica in duck gullets. Sampling in high water, for example, could produce this... But that would NOT prove ducks don't eat it. Finding japonica in hundreds of gullets proves they do."

Which is what Marcial found over years of meticulous autopsies on the waterfowl he killed. Ducks relied heavily on duckgrass. Period. And from his observations, by late November and early December, as soon as the duckgrass is consumed by the waterfowl, the birds leave.

Then Kim Patten testified. After claiming that according to his own study there were several orders of magnitude more duckgrass than could possibly be foraged by waterfowl... he asked the Weed Board if he would be able to spray the duckgrass on his own tidelands, even though they weren't, at that time, commercial shellfish beds.

Marcial's testimony was rebutted by Northern Oyster's Brian Sheldon who testified that only a few species eat duckgrass, that most bird species don't eat it, and *that it was in the way of birds trying to get to their food*, although he did not identify what food he was referring to.

The next day, the Weed Board held its regular meeting. The Sheldons and Patten, were present at this less-attended meeting. The staffperson told the Weed Board that growers told her that if they used a chemical to poison duckgrass, there would be a lot of scrutiny. But if the Weed Board would recognize that duckgrass had a negative economic impact on shellfish production, that designation would provide them with cover. They also talked about duckgrass as the "next spartina."

With the Sheldons and Patten as witnesses, the Weed Board deemed duckgrass a noxious weed on commercial shellfish beds in spite of the detailed evidence Marcial submitted about the critical importance of this plant to migratory waterfowl. Even with his statement juxtaposed with the industry scientist's claim that there was way more duckgrass than the waterfowl needed, followed by the scientist's stated desire to spray his own tidelands. In this unusual ruling, the Weed Board determined duckgrass was *only noxious on commercial shellfish beds*. This bifurcated reasoning was later explained as recognition of both the good and the bad side of duckgrass. Yes, it provided essential ecological functions, and yes, it grew where commercial non-native clam operations were expanding.

As if from out of left field, the shellfish companies then petitioned to have duckgrass listed as a noxious weed *everywhere* in the state. No new scientific evidence was submitted to justify this expansion in listing. For that reason, and due to the level of opposition, the Weed Board's Advisory Committee recommended to the Weed Board that expansion of the listing was not justified in 2012.

The Weed Board held a second hearing that year. That meeting was also held in the high plateau agriculture town of Yakima, an environment hostile to duckgrass, as if the distant and ag-dependent hearing location could foretell its fate. Marcial trekked to Yakima to testify again about the importance of duckgrass. Marcial testified before the shellfish growers and again submitted evidence of significant waterfowl reliance on duckgrass.

And again, at the sparsely attended Weed Board meeting held the day after the contentious hearing, the Sheldons were attendant. The Weed Board listed duckgrass as a *statewide* noxious weed. They determined that duckgrass "...is non-native, difficult to control and negatively impacts the shellfish industry." In 2011, it was a noxious weed only on commercial shellfish beds and now voilà! In 2012, it was a statewide noxious weed.

BAIT AND SWITCH

DFW Director Anderson found himself in an awkward position. When he agreed with the shellfish companies to de-list duckgrass as a priority species in 2011, they told him they only wanted to poison duckgrass on their clam beds in Willapa Bay. Anderson went along, and unilaterally facilitated the removal of duckgrass as a state priority species, even though his managers cautioned that this was a "slippery slope" and that duckgrass was extremely important for wintering waterfowl. Now, in a bait-and-switch maneuver, the shellfish companies got the Weed Board to declare duckgrass noxious statewide and the DFW tried to stop the statewide listing. To no avail.

The listing of duckgrass as a noxious weed statewide in 2012 did not go over well. The Thurston County Noxious Weed Control Board petitioned for a re-consideration and reversion back to the listing just on commercial shellfish beds because they said the beneficial aspects of duckgrass had not been adequately considered by the Weed Board. The other shellfish industry pest, Laura Hendricks and the Coalition to Protect Puget Sound, also filed a petition. Laura observed, "Willapa Bay natural ecological functions have been significantly altered by the shellfish industry spraying carbaryl to eradicate ghost/mud shrimp and glyphosate and imazapyr to eradicate spartina." In addition, Laura said the Weed Board failed to give sufficient weight to scientific evidence including material submitted by DFW, now alarmed at the statewide scope and potential adverse impacts to birds and fish that rely on duckgrass.

The Weed Board had to respond to these petitions. Yet another hearing was scheduled for November 6, 2013.

The third and final hearing was held in Wenatchee. Marcial and his wife, Sophie, packed their car and headed east. They dodged elk as they drove through Packwood, between snow-dusted peaks of the

Cascade Mountain's White Pass, and then dropped down into Yakima and a totally different world. The solid conifer forests thinned to pine trees, dots in open, parched land that was made green here and there by Yakima River basin water. The trip hit a high note for them when they passed Ellensburg, as Sophie had gone to college there while Marcial was at the Naval Academy. The price he paid to be near her during his summer leave was baling hay at the only remaining farm still using antiquated three-wire bales. They laughed as they reflected on the fact that here they were, decades later, driving hundreds of miles into the desert from the coast to make a plea for a marine grass. After five hours on the road, they checked into their Wenatchee hotel.

"The Weed Board is made up of mostly eastern Washington farmers and academics from places like WSU who are friendly to farmers who complain about weeds," Marcial said.

Marcial's heart beat fast and his palms started to sweat. When his six minutes to talk came (three for him; three for Sophie), he was allowed to draw a picture of a duck's gullet: the bill, a long esophagus, an expanded section called the proventriculus, and finally, the gizzard. *Wow,* he thought, *Mother Nature is so amazing.*

While Marcial concentrated on his presentation, Sophie displayed a tray of duck gullets in front of the Weed Board and staff. Marcial made the case that indeed, ducks eat duckgrass and it's not dessert. It's the main course. He emphasized that without duckgrass, the ducks had no food since they did not eat *marina.*

And yet again, much to Marcial's disbelief, without presenting evidence, Brian Sheldon of Northern Oyster Company followed, claiming that while some waterfowl do eat duckgrass, they don't actually require it, and referred instead to "thousands of acres" of some other food that would be available to the ducks in the absence of duckgrass ... and yet again, he did not give any detail about this "other food." In response to this assertion, Marcial simply says, "Duckgrass is not in the way of their food. It is their food."

Over this three-year hearings process, Marcial presented increasingly more evidence to the Weed Board proving that some ducks rely exclusively on duckgrass in Willapa while on their perilous migrations. He presented progressively more detailed information, starting with photos and maps, and ended with actually showing them duck gullets chock full of duckgrass. In contrast, Brian Sheldon presented no pictures, maps, or other evidence, yet claimed the ducks were after other unspecified "critters" and that the duckgrass was in their way.

The next day, at another sparsely attended regular meeting but with the shellfish grower Brian Sheldon attending, the Weed Board continued to insist that duckgrass was a noxious weed everywhere. Others submitted compelling testimony against a statewide listing, including high-profile organizations like the Washington State Invasive Weed Council, Puget Sound Partnership, Thurston Weed Board, the Washington Waterfowl Association and its Grays Harbor chapter, among others. But at the end of the day, the only group that evidently had influence with the Weed Board was the shellfish industry.

The Weed Board justified its decision with: "The non-native species was clearly having a detrimental impact on the shellfish industry (particularly on hardshell clambeds), its ecological impacts in natural areas were positive, negative, and neutral, and complicated."

Unrestricted Open Season on duckgrass brought the shellfish companies dramatically closer to the large-scale eradication of that grass, along with marina, especially if they could convince Ecology to allow destruction of *marina* as collateral damage, and with no buffers. "It's plain as day they want to eliminate both eelgrasses from the bay, duckgrass and *marina*," Marcial observed.

WILLAPA BAY FORTUNE TELLER

Marcial put himself in the shellfish companies' shoes and asked, "What would I do if I wanted to eradicate both eelgrasses?" If he could foretell their strategy to rid eelgrasses in Willapa Bay, he'd know where to look. "I would want duckgrass unprotected. I wouldn't use a surfactant so the imazamox would spread, I'd spray on the incoming tide with no dry time so the water would transport the imazamox in solution. And I'd definitely not want any protective spray buffers for *marina*." He then watched as that plan fell into place. At the final Weed Board hearing, someone tipped Marcial that the shellfish companies purposefully wanted to use imazamox without a surfactant because this allowed greater imazamox distribution in the bay.

Two down: no protection, no surfactant. Two to go.

The third step was to have Ecology de-list duckgrass as critical saltwater habitat with the Shoreline Master Programs.

Done.

Finally, the fourth and final step was to get a permit from the state agency that Marcial called "The Department with the Wrong Name." Ecology.

"The shellfish companies submitted another Patten 'forage budget' to Ecology as part of their permit application environmental analysis," Marcial said. He and a confederate with the Washington Waterfowl Association got a copy of Patten's forage budget.

"The ten gullets I had given him were not in the analysis," Marcial stated. When a wigeon gullet was empty, he logged that as a wigeon that didn't eat duckgrass. But that was actually a wigeon that hadn't eaten lately. We critiqued Patten's forage budget and submitted our analysis to Ecology. Ecology just dropped that version of his forage budget from the documentation, and kept going."

Next, Marcial and his colleague found out another Patten forage budget had appeared. Kim Patten calculated exactly how much duckgrass birds needed to eat in Willapa Bay. According to himself, Patten concluded that 20,000 ducks needed less than 500 acres of duckgrass.

They analyzed this claim too, and Marcial wrote to Ecology that the math was wrong and that other significant factors were not considered. Besides, Marcial knew that come December, after the waterfowl had ravaged the duckgrass until it was gone, they would fly south. In any event, Patten's science provided a touchstone that the shellfish companies could then cite. Brian Sheldon claimed that Patten (his landlord as of 2013) proved that while some waterfowl do eat duckgrass, they don't actually require it.

But this time, Marcial didn't bother Ecology with another deconstruction of Patten's forage budget. He figured Ecology wouldn't listen anyhow. If he had to appeal the likely Ecology permit, he thought this information could be useful in an appeal, where he thought there might be greater reliance on what he considered were facts.

Before Ecology issued their final decision on the permit application, activist and Vietnam War vet Rob Kavanaugh and Laura Hendricks submitted a petition to the DFW Commission to re-list duckgrass as protected.

DFW Commission Chair Miranda Wecker alerted Kim Patten and Richard Wilson, of Bay Center Farms. "We have a petition before the Commission to put japonica back on the Priority Habitat List, meaning WDFW will recommend protecting it. I have not seen any information that would persuade the Commission to order that it be restored to the list, but it would be inappropriate for me to predict how the commission will vote." In another email to them, she wrote, "This petition asks WDFW to put Zj back on the Priority Habitat and Species List. My sense, based on what I have seen in the past, is that

WDFW staff will recommend that the Commission deny this petition. You may want to send in some comments...."

"There was no way out of considering the petition, otherwise I am sure DFW would have dodged that bullet," Marcial speculated. "This unanticipated challenge was dispensed with by the DFW Commission, chaired by Miranda Wecker. The public was not allowed to speak."

Marcial then stated bitterly, "At the end of the meeting, Wecker announced the Commission was now informed about the imazamox permit. But they were not because their staff told them that there was a protective buffer in the permit between the duckgrass and *marina*. There was not. Under the current regime, DFW is a shill for aquaculture takeover and dramatic loss of net ecological function."

In response to an email inquiry, the DFW said they do not know the total acreage of Willapa Bay that has been converted from native habitat to non-native commercial clam farming, or what is planned for conversion. The U.S. Army Corps of Engineers, which permits aquaculture and normally prohibits bay-wide filling, could not produce a tally of how much gravel has been filled into Willapa Bay to date, or shells. Gravel is primarily filled into the nearshore tidelands to firm up the sediments for non-native clam farming. Ecology doesn't know either.

There is no record of an environmental impact statement asking what impact the industrial-scale mono-crop farming of non-native oysters and clams is having on the ecosystem, including the cumulative impacts of continuous pesticide use since 1963, and the major filling of the bay with gravel and oyster shells, the harrowing, cutting eelgrass, and the dredging.

The environmental impact statements prepared to date in Willapa Bay instead focus on pesticide approval.

Ecology issued the imazamox final environmental analysis in

March 2014, followed by a five-year permit to the Shellfish Association to annually spray unlimited acres of duckgrass and *marina* in Willapa Bay with imazamox, just in time for the newly created April to June spray season.

In 2014, Ecology gave them permission to spray an unprecedented 3,000 acres of tideland with imazamox, including known forage fish spawning area and Pacific Brant feeding areas.

At year-end, they reported spraying 300 acres. Marcial noted that they claimed ducks would not be harmed based on Kim Patten's determination that there was more than enough eelgrass to go around. But he observed that the birds left when they had consumed all the eelgrass and suspected that if there had been more, the ducks would have eaten it too.

NATIVE EELGRASS ERADICATED

Ecology also gave approval to spray the native eelgrass: *marina*. Marcial was dumbstruck that Ecology would allow the loss of so many aquatic plants, including the native *marina*. (Concerns were also raised that the herbicide Imazamox would kill the very small microalgae and phytoplankton in the bay—critical food for native species.)

"Ecology promised buffers between the two species. There are none. No inventory was required of how much duckgrass or *marina* was killed, and no restoration plan was devised," Marcial said. "The Department with the Wrong Name told the public not to worry. Only a few hundred acres a year would be killed. Of course, as duckgrass and *marina* habitat was converted to non-commercial clam habitat, it would never be restored. It would become an expanded shellfish operation. Herring spawn in eelgrass beds of both species. DFW has not measured herring spawning in Willapa Bay since then," Marcial reported. "That first 3,000 acres allowed to be poisoned included mapped herring spawning beds!" Marcial said incredulously.

The imazamox environmental documents were drafted by Shellfish Association members and their consultant. They state one of the purposes of poisoning duckgrass was "to maintain the beneficial uses of state waters." The final document concluded that there would be no adverse impacts to waterfowl from the loss of up to 2,000 acres of duckgrass. "The reduction in Z. japonica (duckgrass) on Willapa Bay commercial clam beds is not expected to adversely affect waterfowl."

Audubon's Bayard wrote a letter in protest of spraying the duckgrass and *marina*:

> Although Z. japonica (duckgrass) is a non-native species and is listed as a noxious weed in Washington, there is no scientific consensus that it degrades nearshore ecosystems or habitat quality for birds or fish. Indeed, there are a number of studies demonstrating its value as food and habitat, including as an important food source for waterfowl such as brant, northern pintail and mallard... Documents filed by the Washington State Noxious Weed Board describe their rationale for listing Z. japonica as a noxious weed:
>
> "Zostera japonica (duckgrass) was listed as a Class C noxious weed for 2013 because it was recognized as a non-native, difficult to control species that was negatively impacting the shellfish industry, regardless of beneficial functions it may provide in natural tidelands."

Others wrote in too, but by now, who would expect Ecology to do anything but issue another pesticide permit?

Which they did, with no eelgrass eradication acreage limit, or meaningful monitoring. All major four steps had been consummated over a brief, four-year whirlwind.

CITIZEN APPEAL TO POLITICALLY-APPOINTED BOARD...

Marcial, and a few others, fought every step of the way to this point. His data and observations were swept away with all others questioning the science primarily provided by Patten. Marcial thought maybe the state's Governor-appointed Pollution Control Hearings Board (Board) would see reason. What choice did he have? So Marcial joined with Rob Kavanagh and Laura Hendricks to appeal the Ecology permit to destroy essential bird and fish habitat in Willapa Bay.

They filed their appeal. In the meantime, Shellfish Association members sprayed in 2014. The scheduling of their appeal dragged on. The Shellfish Association sprayed again in 2015, two full years in a row, with Marcial's appeal pending. One state clam tenant, Long Island Oyster, sprayed and left the "cooperating landowner" section of their spray plan blank. No notice was provided to the state to kill duckgrass and *marina* on publicly owned land.

As Marcial watched, 85 percent of the duckgrass and eelgrass died throughout the Nemah River flats where Marcial lives. The closest Ecology-authorized spray site was 6,000 feet away, more than one mile to the west of Marcial's property. The area actually sprayed was even further. The grasses on his tidelands, instead of growing during the spring and summer seasons, receded. By 95 percent. Normally, by August, the grasses were peaking. Now, they were almost entirely gone. According to Marcial, "Contrary to all the promises made, the imazamox's toxicity was not confined to just the 'sprayed' sites, as asserted by the Shellfish Association in the FEIS and Ecology. They are almost completely gone now."

Almost at a loss for knowing where to begin, Marcial regains his composure and says, "These grasses are the food for northern pintail. Pintail are the only dabbling duck not exceeding their long-term average at present. The whole southern third of the bay has been defoliated of vital grasses. Ecology relied on dilution, but this part of the bay doesn't 'flush' like they fantasized it would. The loss of the grasses affects herring spawning, salmon, ducks, and Brants in the southern half of the bay. It's unbelievable.

"The chums are in trouble. When I moved here full-time in 2001/2002, the Nemah River—you'd think you were in Alaska! Wall to wall chum salmon with coho mixed in. The chum salmon took a nosedive associated with spartina spraying. They tried to come back after spartina spraying stopped. The fish didn't come back very well because our elected officials and DFW let them get hammered by gillnetters. They have not been allowed to come back.

"Now, depending on how much imazamox they spray, they may never come back! Chum smolts depend on duckgrass and *marina* for their survival. Period. Chums immediately come down river as little fry and spend 99 percent of their juvenile stage in the bay and nowhere else. They are here from the end of February through May. Not only are they exposed to this new pesticide, imazamox has wiped out the grasses that juvenile chum need for cover from predators and for forage. Without the grasses, they get hammered by predators."

The appeal of the imazamox permit was finally heard on October 7, 2015, a year and a half after it was submitted. After two full years of spraying.

The hearing lasted three grueling days.

"The president of the Washington Waterfowl Association and I showed the Board the record low numbers of waterfowl counts in Willapa Bay for early November to late October, 2012 through 2015:

Year	Ducks
2012	100,000
2013	70,000

2014   22,000 (first full year of imazamox spraying)
2015   14,000 (second full year of imazamox spraying)

"In 2014, even more alarming than the dramatic overall drop in waterfowl, was the breakdown of waterfowl by area. In the area that encompasses the highest concentration of spraying, there were only 32 wigeon and zero pintail seen from the plane! Since then, we received the counts for November 2015. The peak in November was a measly 14,000 ducks!" Marcial said sadly. (After 2015, the state quit counting but Marcial estimated 8,000 in 2016 and 12,000 in 2017. He was present in the bay for earlier counts and had a good base for comparison.)

After day two of the hearing, Marcial's intuition was that at least one of the judges was a "no" vote. As it turned out, it was a unanimous "no" vote. The Shellfish Association had the approval of the Governor-appointed Pollution Control Hearings Board to continue spraying imazamox into Willapa Bay.

WATERFOWL IN DECLINE? WHO'S COUNTING?

Upon entering Marcial's house, guests are tempted to call 911 to report a ransacking. Piles of papers, books, and documents cover an invisible dining room table. A casually placed book on top of this trove of information is entitled, *The Life-Changing Magic of Tidying Up*, by Marie Kondo. Marcial quips that even talking about neatness is a waste of valuable time. "I haven't read the book. I don't need it. That's my wife's book. It's lost in the clutter."

While his nest may be a bit cluttered, his mind is sharp. Marcial is able to see the pieces of the ecosystem and read what is happening as if reading a book. The story is there to see, all that is needed is to observe. And he is observing. Where are the birds?

"During the spartina spraying—which also poisoned *marina* and duckgrass—the state stopped counting ducks. After the spraying wound down, DFW started counting ducks again in 2012. When they first started, they were doing six or eight counts starting in September when the ducks start to show up, and continued into January. Now, they just do the usual winter count in January when most are gone, even in the best of years. They aren't capturing the true picture.

And DFW staff agree. They say that due to lack of funding, they are not able to count the waterfowl to determine what impact the poisoning of the duckgrass is having. All they are doing is a count in January, which is merely a snapshot in time, coordinated with a nationwide count.

DFW staff say that one count informs what is going on big picture; it isn't the way to get at what is going on locally. They went on to say that any connection between spraying duckgrass and waterfowl would require much more effort than what DFW is doing.

"On top of that, they aren't counting the Brant. For the last three years, I asked for the Brant numbers. First, I asked DFW. They said they were no longer counting the Brant, and that they had transferred this job over to the Willapa Refuge three years ago. So I asked the refuge for numbers and got a run-around. This year I demanded it from the DFW. Again, they referred me to the Refuge. I pressed them. They referred me to someone else. Finally, I had an answer: The Refuge doesn't count the spring staging Brant anymore; only a less useful winter count."

"I couldn't find any staging Brant this spring (2016). I've talked to the Willapa Refuge Manager, and she's all on board with getting rid of the duckgrass. She told me the ducks are back ... but they aren't. Look at the counts," Marcial said. "When the refuge manager says, 'The ducks are back,' and they are half of what the refuge historically carried, you have a problem. So that's what we are up against. They don't allow hunting on most of the refuge, but they allow duck food to be killed. The refuge is now giving tours of the site of its new multi-million-dollar headquarters. It might be put on top of a goose pasture."

Marcial is convinced that the Willapa National Wildlife Refuge has forgotten why it is there: "The Wildlife Refuge was established in 1937 by President Franklin D. Roosevelt to protect migrating birds and their habitat at a time when many estuaries and shallow water bays were being destroyed in the name of progress."

"Willapa Bay water stays in the south bay for an average 45-day residency. South of Long Island, it's 60 days. So what goes in the Wildlife Refuge area stays there. Imazamox is harming all the grasses," Marcial sums up. "There is no *marina* south of Long Island, it's all gone. As a direct result, there are few if any Brant south of Long Island in the wildlife refuge created for birds, where historically there were thousands. They normally had a weak crop of duckgrass but it could not hold the ducks very long. Now, the whole bay can't hold them very long. But who's checking? The permit has no acreage limit and requires no meaningful monitoring. If you don't count the ducks or the Brant, and you don't inventory the grasses in the bay, there's no problem."

What is happening to our migratory birds? In the meantime, pesticide use continues.

No baseline, no monitoring, no problem.

EPILOGUE

On March 13, 2018, Hilary Franz, the elected head of the Department of Natural Resources, announced with fanfare a plan to spend more than $1,000,000 in public funds to combat native shrimp in Willapa Bay—one of which is widely believed to be headed to extinction. Because, according to Franz, the state needs to "stem the expanding burrowing shrimp populations." The same shrimp the state has been poisoning for more than fifty years.[18]

Oddly, although the state now has millions to spend on the war on burrowing shrimp, they can't come up with a relatively small amount ($1,500 to $2,000 for plane rental plus staff time per trip) for a few extra waterfowl counts in October and November, to better capture how the Shellfish Association's poisoning of the Pacific Flyway American wigeon, northern pintail, mallard, dusky, and brant's primary food—eelgrass—could be impacting their vulnerable migrations.

Spraying of imazamox to kill the eelgrass began in 2014 in Willapa Bay, and continues to this day with only one count in January instead of at least two counts per month in October,

---

[18] In 2016, DNR prepared a report about shrimp harvest and gray whale feeding, but only in Puget Sound in response to the City of Langley's concerns about shrimp populations. A similar analysis was not prepared for Willapa Bay.

November, December, and January—ideally with ground observations as to habitat use—that DFW staff say is necessary to fully understand how the spraying of eelgrass is impacting the waterfowl.

Not enough money? Or no priority to protect native species and habitats?

In addition, the state says it is now considering funding on-going anti-shrimp measures, as well as paying for shellfish growing directly via public grants. Yet again, compare this major public funding effort against Ecology's historical position that it didn't have enough money to monitor anything but the wind speed for the annual spraying of carbaryl.

Some of this new-found money will be spent to re-study mechanical attacks on the native shrimp: harrowing, suffocating and blasting—to aid the non-native shellfish industry. The state says the ultimate goal of the project is to protect the shellfish industry, but cautions that this initiative might be perceived as giving preferential treatment to one industry, and giving away state assets.

Franz also announced that DNR will identify "unused tidelands" that could be made available to impacted oyster farmers. Unused tidelands? What about the birds? What about the shrimp? What about the eelgrasses, native worms, salmon, and herring? What about people who enjoy the already limited public tidelands on Willapa Bay? Unused appears to mean *unused by the shellfish industry*.

Sturgeon are endangered, and burrowing shrimp are a staple of their diet. Can the sturgeon get to the shrimp through sharp oyster shells? How has the perpetual assaults on the native shrimp impacted the sturgeon? How is the dumping of barge-loads of gravel into Willapa Bay nearshore tidelands for non-native clam culture impacting native habitat and species? Are these native species considered disposable by the state?

Then, for the first time in almost sixty years, on April 9, 2018, the state, via Ecology, announced that it was "tentatively denying" the Shellfish Association's re-submittal to use imidacloprid in Willapa Bay and Grays Harbor.

In the meantime, the Shellfish Association continues to spray Willapa Bay eelgrasses with imazamox, and the state says it isn't monitoring how this is impacting the vulnerable migratory birds.

But the larger policy question remains to be asked and answered: Why is the state allowing the conversion of our marine ecosystems into huge non-native shellfish farms to feed far-flung human populations—at the expense of our native species?

APPENDIX A: PESTICIDE-SPRAYING COMPANIES

PERMITTED CARBARYL INSECTICIDE USERS

WILLAPA BAY

    E.H. Bendicksen Co. (former Taylor Shellfish Landlord)

    Taylor Shellfish

    Coast Seafoods

    Bay Center Mariculture (Dick Wilson)

    Wiegardt & Sons

    Northern Oyster Company (Sheldons)

    Ekone

    Jambor Oyster

    Nisbet Oyster Company

    Goose Point Oyster Company

    R&B Oyster Company

    Heckes Oyster Company

    Heckes Clam Company

    Heckes Clam and Oyster Company

    Olsen & Son

    Stony Point Oyster Company

    Willapa Fish and Oyster

Willapa Bay Shellfish
Watkins Oyster Co.
Long Island Oyster Company
Parson Oyster Co.
South Bend Packers
Oysterville Sea Farms
Petit & Sons
Washington Department of Fish & Wildlife
Elkhorn Oyster
Wilson Oyster Company
G.A. Wiegardt
Moore Oysters
Gillies
Herrold Fish & Oyster
Hendrickson
University of Washington School of Fisheries
Hall & Wooley
R. Brian Kemmer
James Kemmer
David Nisbet

GRAYS HARBOR

Coast Seafoods
Grass Creek Oyster Company
Markham Enterprises
Associated Seafoods
Brady's Oysters
Northwest Oyster
Hemlock Hollow
Roger Johnson

Cedar River Oyster
Cedar River Seafoods
Chenois Creek
Lytle
Bay Fish
Johansen

Permitted Imidacloprid Insecticide Users

The companies sprayed imidacloprid on 426 acres in Willapa Bay, and on 130 acres in Grays Harbor.

WILLAPA BAY and GRAYS HARBOR
Taylor Shellfish
Coast Seafoods
Wiegardt & Sons
Bay Center Mariculture
Northern Oyster Company
Heckes Clams
Jambor Oyster
Nisbet Oyster
R&B Oyster
Stoney Point Oyster
Willapa Fish and Oyster
Markham Oyster
G.A. & Lila Wiegardt

Permitted Imazamox Herbicide Users In Willapa Bay

Long Island Oyster
Station House Oysters
Taylor Shellfish Company
Wiegardt and Sons
Northern Oyster Company
Willapa Bay Shellfish
Herrold Fish & Oyster
Heckes Clam Inc.
Coast Seafoods

CHAPTER NOTES

The Notes can be found at www.toxicpearl.com.